Fieldwork at A level: Your guide to the independent investigation

Dave Holmes, Daniel House, Peter Knight, Dave Morgan, Simon Norman, Simon Oakes, Robin Sutton, Richard Waller

Editor: Simon Oakes

Geographical Association

The Geographical Association is the leading subject association for all teachers of geography. Our charitable mission is to further geographical knowledge and understanding through education. Our journals, publications, professional events, website and local and online networks support teachers and share their ideas and practice. The GA represents the views of geography teachers and plays a leading role in public debate relating to geography and education.

ISBN 978-1-84377-418-1

First published 2018
Impression number 10 9 8 7 6 5 4 3 2
Published by the Geographical Association, 160 Solly Street, Sheffield S1 4BF
Company number 07139068

Website: www.geography.org.uk
E-mail: info@geography.org.uk

The Geographical Association is a registered charity: no 1135148

Cover images: © Simon Oakes/Bryan Ledgard
Copy edited by Louise Morris
Cartography/illustrations by Paul Coles
Designed and typeset by Bryan Ledgard
Printed and bound in UK by W & G Baird

Disclaimer: Every effort has been made to identify and contact the original sources of copyright material. If there have been any inadvertent breaches of copyright we apologise and will make corrections at the first opportunity.

Contents

Introduction 4

1 Establishing a focus and setting up your enquiry 6

2 Data collection and analysis 14

3 Using GIS in your investigation 25

4 Investigating human environments 34

5 Investigating physical environments 46

6 Evaluating your findings and presenting your work 61

Glossary 67

Online resources

There are additional materials accompanying this book that are available to download. These include skills and information sheets.

To access these go to **www.geography.org.uk/fieldwork** then click on the button for this book. You will then be asked for your password.

The unique password for this book is SO18F1

Introduction

Fieldwork-based enquiry makes teaching and learning in geography different from the study of other humanities and social science subjects. Geography students get to apply their skills in an out-of-class context. They critically explore how well classroom models and theories fit with more complex real-world contexts. Real independence of thought is nurtured when learners are allowed to devise their own unique enquiry focus. In these and other ways, the Non-Examined Assessment (NEA) adds value to your geographical education irrespective of whether you are proceeding either to higher education or directly to employment.

Department for Education A level geography NEA criteria

The independent investigation may relate to human or physical geography or it may integrate them. The independent investigation must:
- be based on a question or issue defined and developed by the student individually to address aims, questions and/or hypotheses relating to any of the compulsory or optional content
- incorporate field data and/or evidence from field investigations, collected individually or in groups
- draw on the student's own research, including their own field data and, if relevant, secondary data sourced by the student
- require the student independently to contextualise, analyse and summarise findings and data
- involve the individual drawing of conclusions and their communication by means of extended writing and the presentation of relevant data.

Source: *Geography GCE AS and A level subject content December 2014* Reference: DFE-00693-2014 © DfE

Well-designed fieldwork is one of the most memorable experiences students have at school. It provides inspiration, develops practical, group work and leadership skills and increases independence. Geographical Association

Fieldwork inspires; it is hands-on real-world learning, allowing students to make meaning of the landscapes and cities they live in. It is an integral part of geography and offers opportunities for personal and academic development and collaboration. Fieldwork takes us to new places where we explore, develop and experience, improving our geographical skills. Field Studies Council

Photo: Simon Oakes

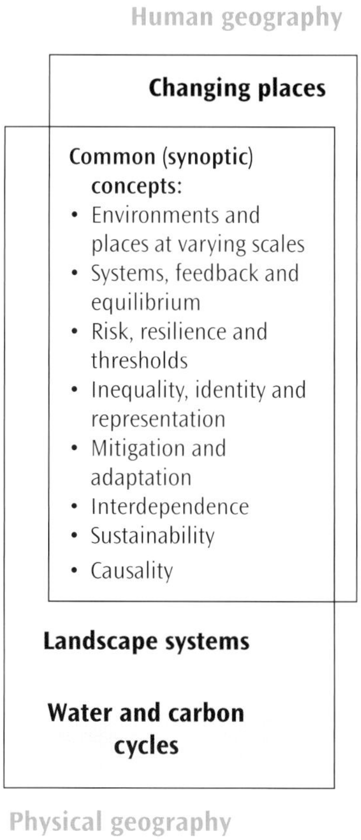

Changing places

Common (synoptic) concepts:
- Environments and places at varying scales
- Systems, feedback and equilibrium
- Risk, resilience and thresholds
- Inequality, identity and representation
- Mitigation and adaptation
- Interdependence
- Sustainability
- Causality

Landscape systems

Water and carbon cycles

Physical geography

Figure 0.1: Common concepts for fieldwork in A level human and physical geography

Between 2008 and 2016, the NEA (or 'independent investigation') was not a component of geography courses in the UK. The inclusion of an NEA in the latest A level specifications therefore provides students with an exciting new learning opportunity. Recent developments in technology mean that fieldwork today can be carried out using tools like smartphones which were not available in the past. This has opened up all kinds of new possibilities for researchers. However, the strengthened requirement for A level learners to work independently and to become highly skilled in a range of **quantitative** and/or **qualitative** data research techniques, may at first seem daunting to some students. This book lends support as you embark on a rewarding but sometimes challenging path of real-world engagement, learning and reflection. Particular aims are to:

- help you find a topic focus (but without doing all of your thinking for you!)
- ensure you fully understand the enquiry cycle which underpins the NEA
- demonstrate a wide range of possible skills, approaches and methods (both qualitative and quantitative) in your investigation
- prepare you for different ways of analysing your fieldwork data following the information collection stage
- guide you through the goals and pitfalls of the writing-up process.

Chapter	Focus	What the chapter covers
1	Getting started with your individual investigation	Deciding on a topic, setting up the enquiry, establishing hypotheses.
2	The different types of data that geographers collect and make use of	Ensuring your quantitative and qualitative data is collected in well-informed, rigorous and bias-free ways. Analysing your data.
3	The value of geographical information systems (GIS) and corresponding software packages	Considering possible roles for GIS in fieldwork planning, data collection, data presentation and data analysis.
4 and 5	Core topics for fieldwork in A level human and physical geography (see Figure 0.1)	Using your fieldwork in the investigation. Ways in which your investigation can make use of core topic ideas, including enquiry focus suggestions.*
6	Writing up your individual investigation	Formatting and presenting your material, plus guidance on conclusions.

* All students *must devise their own title* independently so long lists of possible titles have not been provided.

The most important message this book offers is that students are most likely to make a success of their individual investigation when they view it as an exciting challenge rather than a chore. The A level geography curriculum gives you an opportunity to take full ownership of the learning process for a topic of your own choice; a topic which really interests and motivates *you*. With proper up-front thought and planning – the importance of which is stressed repeatedly here – you may surprise yourself and others with what you can achieve working independently.

Top Tips

Top tips are provided throughout this book. These aim to highlight good fieldwork practice and to make you aware of common fieldwork mistakes and misconceptions.

References

- Tilling, S. (2016) *A year of fieldwork: why do we need it?* Field Studies Council http://www.field-studies-council. org/media/ 2653667/tilling-eis-2016.pdf

1 Establishing a focus and setting up your enquiry

Objectives

- *Understand the purpose(s) of fieldwork, to allow you to develop sound objectives for your own investigation.*

- *Understand the different stages of the enquiry process, from start to finish, and recognise the different kinds of geographic contexts and data you could make use of along your enquiry pathway.*

- *Understand how to begin finding a research focus or question which is appropriate to your A level geography course.*

The purpose of the independent investigation

Planning and undertaking your own investigation is a good opportunity to confirm and test geographical assumptions or established theories. However, the independent investigation can also present a challenge; it requires skills of organisation, motivation and, as its title suggests, independence. Often, many of the problems that arise during an independent investigation can be predicted and managed beforehand. It's all down to good planning.

Most commonly, successful investigations will have tackled geographical ideas which are linked to changes occurring over space and/or time. Key questions to ask at the very start of the enquiry process are:
- Is the work geographical and linked in a clear and meaningful way to a content area contained within your A level geography specification?
- Is any planned survey work manageable and achievable in terms of its scale, location and accessibility?
- How much time and equipment will be needed?
- Does your initial background research into the topic indicate whether any high-quality supporting data and information have been published previously?
- Does the focus you have chosen link with any other geographical topics and issues so that it can be framed usefully within a 'bigger picture'?

The benefits of high quality fieldwork

A recent report (Lambert and Reiss, 2016) confirms the significance of high-quality fieldwork as an integral part of being a fully competent geographer. Figure 1.1 shows some reflective ideas that might form part of your initial thinking about investigation. A good investigation will help build your skills, competencies and capabilities because they will become embedded in the work you carry out.

Lambert and Reiss are interested also in the notion of 'messy' geography. This means that the world is often far more complex than textbooks suggest. As a result, fieldwork data are also often harder to interpret and draw meaning from than some students might first expect. Creating fieldwork data and research information which challenge **orthodox** geographical models and assumptions can be an exciting and enriching experience.

Reflective ideas	Skills, competencies and capabilities
Will I be able to apply and evaluate my prior geographic knowledge and understanding?	• Competencies in data handling and statistical understanding become embedded in fieldwork. • Background research includes the review of relevant available literature and selective use of secondary materials; can also develop **synthesis** (linking) skills. • May help with the acquisition of technology skills, e.g. spreadsheet manipulation or analysis using **GIS**. • May help develop skills in working with 'big data' sets.
Will I extend and develop my knowledge through new 'deeper' learning?	• Fieldwork helps us 'see' learned things differently and in a new context. • Encourages caution, reflectivity and creativity in data analysis. • Enables critical thinking and may provide an opportunity to challenge the 'accepted' view about a topic issue or relationship. • Helps with skills of reasoning as well as encouraging geographical curiosity.
What transferable social skills can I develop doing fieldwork?	• Fieldwork helps foster independent and reflective learning. • Teaches procedural skills and knowledge which are transferable to other situations and subjects. • Greater awareness of ethical considerations can be an important as part of the enquiry process. Creates an atmosphere for cooperation in problem solving.

Figure 1.1 Reflections on fieldwork: high quality experience can help develop student knowledge, skills, competencies and capabilities.
Source: Adapted from Lambert and Reiss (2016)

Fieldwork or coursework?

Fieldwork and coursework are not the same things although they may overlap. Fieldwork is correctly described as a first-hand experience gained by students *working outside the classroom*. In contrast, coursework is a document produced by a student forming part of an assessment or qualification. Some past and present geography courses include coursework which is based upon a fieldwork experience. The 2016 A level geography qualification requires that fieldwork is carried out to support an *independent investigation* rather than coursework. The proper name for this independent investigation is the Non-Examined Assessment, or NEA.

The enquiry process

What is meant by an enquiry?

Fieldwork is an integral part of a geographical enquiry. A true enquiry:
• is both driven by and stimulates a student's 'need to know'
• makes use of real-world data and information
• requires us to make sense of geographical information
• is reflective (makes us ask questions about how and what we are learning and what approaches work best when undertaking an enquiry).

A geographic enquiry is based on a series of discrete stages or procedures. You will probably find this approach familiar because the scientific route to enquiry uses a similar sequence.

Figure 1.2 Aspects of the enquiry process which underpin the A level geography independent investigation.

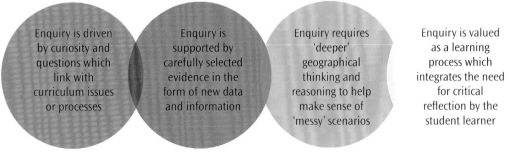

Enquiry is driven by curiosity and questions which link with curriculum issues or processes

Enquiry is supported by carefully selected evidence in the form of new data and information

Enquiry requires 'deeper' geographical thinking and reasoning to help make sense of 'messy' scenarios

Enquiry is valued as a learning process which integrates the need for critical reflection by the student learner

The current A level geography qualification has its own similar (but more detailed) enquiry model of investigation shown in Figure 1.3. Understanding this approach is important as it forms the basis and structure of the NEA mark scheme.

Figure 1.3 The A level geography 5-stage model of enquiry. **Source**: Adapted from DfE geography criteria, December 2014

Stage	Description
1 Purpose; identification of a suitable question/ aim/ **hypothesis** and developing a focus	• Identify appropriate field research questions/aims/hypotheses, based on knowledge and understanding of relevant aspects of physical and/or human geography. • Research the relevant literature sources linked to possible fieldwork opportunities presented by the environment, considering their practicality and relationship to compulsory and optional taught subject content. • Understand the nature of the current literature research relevant to the focus. This should be clearly and appropriately referenced within the written report.
2 Designing fieldwork and research **methodologies**; selection of appropriate equipment and techniques	• Think about how best to observe and record geographical ideas in the field and how to design appropriate data collection and sampling strategies, which account for the frequency and timing of observations. • Design good field methodologies (for primary data) which are appropriate to the investigation and may select a combination of qualitative and quantitative techniques. • Show an understanding of the ethical dimensions of conducting field research.
3 Data; collation and presentation	• Know how to use appropriate diagrams, graphs and maps. • Use **geospatial** technologies to support relevant aspects of the investigation and its outcomes.
4 Analysis; interpretation and explanation of results and data	• Use appropriate techniques to analyse field data and research information. • Write a coherent analysis of fieldwork findings and results (linked consistently to a specific geographical focus).
5 Conclusions and evaluation; critical reflection on methods and results	• Use knowledge and understanding (including theories and concepts) to interpret meaning from the investigation, draw comparisons and ask reflective questions. • Demonstrate the ability to critically examine field data (including any measurement errors) in order to comment on their accuracy and/or the extent to which they are **representative** and reliable. • Explain how the results relate to any wider geographical contexts and use the experience to extend geographical understanding.

Avoiding an enquiry 'deficit'

Some academics and professional geographers have been critical of schools' geography for sometimes neglecting key aspects of the enquiry process. This alleged 'deficit' is shown in Figure 1.4. According to this argument, too much attention is paid to the blue circles and not enough to the orange ones.

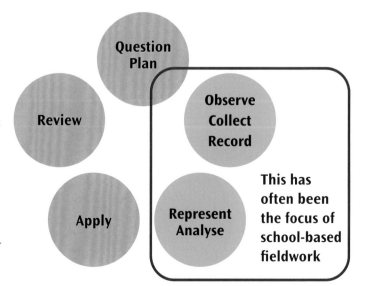

Figure 1.4 School-based fieldwork and enquiry have focused traditionally on data collection and presentation (blue), rather than *all* aspects of the enquiry process (orange).
Source: David Holmes

Where the full breadth of the enquiry process is not used, as Figure 1.4 suggests, a number of worrying issues may arise:

1 It becomes harder to make the conceptual leap which is required to 'join the dots' between text-book theories and models and the often complex (and messy) data that real fieldwork generates.
2 The main focus of the enquiry becomes a series of repetitious tasks based on measuring and recording. While 'jumping through hoops' we are missing opportunities to engage more critically with research and exploration processes.
3 The enquiry's possible links with wider geographical ideas become under-valued and neglected. As a result, any evaluation of the study's findings may be limited and perfunctory.
4 Woking in a purely **deductive** style and not reflecting on enquiry design in an **inductive** way can become self-limiting. A purely deductive inquiry can constrain critical thinking and thoughtful evaluation (Figure 1.5).

Figure 1.5 Aspects of the inductive and deductive models of inquiry; depending on your topic, you may need to choose between these approaches. **Source**: http://research-methodology.net/research-methodology

Deductive work (a 'traditional' approach)	Inductive work (a 'progressive' approach)
• A deductive approach is concerned with developing a hypothesis (or hypotheses) based on existing theory and then designing a research strategy to test the hypothesis. • A deductive approach follows the path of logic closely. • Deduction begins with an expected pattern that is tested against field observations.	• This involves asking new questions during and after data collection, as new evidence comes to light; theories can be formulated towards the end of the research as a result of the study's observations. • The researcher may be unsure about what the research findings show until the entire study is completed; induction begins with observations and looks for a pattern within them.

Finding a focus and location for your enquiry

Coming up with *your own* geographical idea or enquiry focus can be one of the most challenging aspects of the independent investigation. It could be based around a local topical issue, or may relate to something that you have read about or studied previously (though, importantly, the topic must be clearly relevant to geography). If you visit a field

Figure 1.6 Examples of geographical themes that could be investigated by members of a geography class visiting a rural, coastal environment. **Source**: Carol Bulmer

Over to you
Repeat this exercise for a photo of a town centre you are interested in studying. How many research questions can you generate when you start thinking critically about the image? Think as widely as you can across as many geography topics as possible, including physical geography.

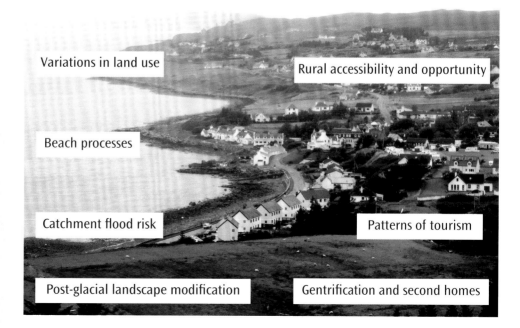

Geological influences on landscape

Microclimate variations

Variations in land use

Rural accessibility and opportunity

Beach processes

Catchment flood risk

Patterns of tourism

Post-glacial landscape modification

Gentrification and second homes

centre, you will be given opportunities to work in a particular outdoors environment. However, you must still devise *your own* individual title. Teachers and field centre staff are not meant to assist you with this.

Even places which seem relatively familiar can offer an opportunity for geographical enquiry; it may be just a case of looking at them in a new light. A detailed analysis of your geography specification might also pay dividends. Figure 1.7 shows some of the core topics in the 2016 A level geography criteria which can serve as fieldwork topic areas.

Figure 1.7 A level geography core topics (all courses) can provide ideas for an individual investigation.

Water and carbon cycles (also see chapter 5)	• **Carbon cycling** on different scales. • Local water stores and pathways. • Land use changes and physical systems.
Landscape systems (also see chapter 5)	• Physical processes, energy flows and **geomorphological** features. • Characteristics of landforms and landscapes. • Landscape system management.
Changing places (also see chapter 4)	• Relationships and connections between different places. • Inequality and differences between and/or within places. • Meanings, representations and ways of managing places.
Global systems and global governance (not covered in depth in this book)	• Flows of international migrants and the resulting issues and impacts. • Impacts of globalisation on places and local reactions against global flows. • How global governance influences the management of local areas.

What types of data are you interested in?

While at this initial stage of the enquiry process, it is useful to start thinking about what your balance between different types of data might be.
- Primary data are first-hand data collected by students themselves (working individually, or as part of a group).
- Secondary data means information that has already been collected by someone else (in geography, this is generally viewed as either raw data or a completed analysis which someone else has carried out, for example data collected as part of an AS or previous investigation).
- Quantitative data consists of numerical and **frequency data** which can be tabulated, tested statistically or converted into charts and graphs.
- Qualitative data are non-numerical observations and descriptions of phenomena. They include in-depth interviews with people (which may read like excerpts from an autobiography), photographs, novels, poems, paintings and even music.

Carrying out a background information and literature review

Having established the geographical idea and context you want to work with, the next stage is to begin the literature review. The purpose of this is to get important background information which is used in a variety of ways. You can use previously published reports, maps and data to:
- virtually explore the context or place where you will be working
- get the most up-to-date thinking and current published information about your topic
- find out more about local people's views and opinions as a starting point for your own work
- explore geographical models and theories that may be relevant to your enquiry focus.

Original documents and research papers can also show you how ideas have developed over time about a particular feature, process or place.

Top Tip
Blending your data
Do not worry about achieving a perfect blend of qualitative and quantitative approaches. Both are valuable to an enquiry, but the balance will depend on your topic choice and its research focus. Physical topics may lean more towards frequency data but try to also make use of some qualitative information (e.g. photographs of buildings in a flood risk area). Some human topics will favour a qualitative approach (e.g. in-depth interviews with local residents) but quantitative data can play an important part in 'setting the scene' (e.g. official unemployment figures for the survey area).

The background information search kick-starts the enquiry process. It is the beginning of your search for answers and should take place well ahead of stepping out of the classroom to begin your primary (first-hand) data collection. This literature review is a vital part of mature research. Do make sure, however, that you evaluate the usefulness and trustworthiness of the information you uncover. Look critically at the age of the data. Who is the author? Are you reading facts or opinions? Are the research findings backed up by the work of other authors?

Finally, the literature review may be important in helping you determine an appropriate geographical scale to work at. A successful independent investigation outcome depends partly on making the right choice here. For instance, an investigation into a large town or city's flood risk is unlikely to arrive at a significant and meaningful context if you only collect data from one small part of the catchment and ignore the wider urban context. Background reading on the city and its river would show you this at the outset; you might then decide to narrow your enquiry focus to a single tributary river, making the enquiry scale suitable for study within the realms of the A level NEA. .

Natural systems and landscape systems often display considerable variability within a very small area. Figure 1.8 shows a geology map (freely available online): vital background information for many physical geography study topics. Using this map, a student can identify a small **homogeneous** (uniform) area to work in; or perhaps a small area with **heterogeneous** (varied) geological characteristics.

Figure 1.8 A geology map can provide vital background information about the geomorphology of a local place and its wider spatial context.
Source: http://www.bgs.ac.uk/discoveringGeology/geologyOfBritain/viewer.html

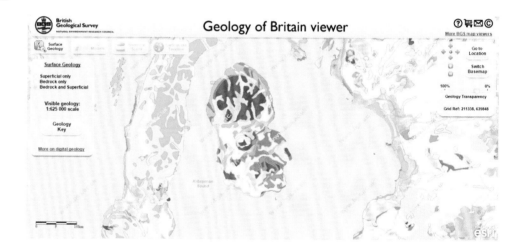

Establishing achievable enquiry goals

Figure 1.9 shows the difference between an aim, a question and a hypothesis – all of which can serve as enquiry goals. Research aims, questions and hypotheses generally fall into two main types:
- those that focus on **spatial** (areal) or temporal (time) *differences*
- those that focus on *relationships* between variables.

Whatever the focus of your individual investigation, there must be a clear geographical element and an obvious linkage to the specification. It is up to you to decide how many questions or hypotheses are appropriate for your enquiry. It is possible to use a 'mix and match' approach. You might adopt a single over-arching aim (for example: 'To investigate the success of the rebranding of Cardiff') which is then explored using several different sub-questions (for example: 'How successful are flagship projects such as Cardiff's Dr Who exhibition?' (now closed)).

Aim	Question	Hypothesis / null hypothesis
A statement of what your geographical enquiry wants to achieve. A well-thought-out enquiry aim will be geographically sound and achievable. • *'An investigation into the effectiveness of traffic calming measures in Leeds.'* • *'An investigation into the reliability and variability of regional weather forecasts when compared with local primary data in Wimbledon.'*	Key research question(s) are used to frame the enquiry. One question may serve as the overall enquiry title, while additional questions are used to help sub-divide the written report. • *'How and why do beach profiles vary along a short stretch of coastline?'* • *'To what extent are golf courses an environmental, economic and social asset in Wiltshire?'*	A hypothesis is a statement whose accuracy can be tested objectively using scientific methodology. You may also be familiar with the use of null hypotheses in science lessons. • *'Most shoppers in Southport purchase goods and services at least once a week.'* • *'There is no significant difference between the gradient of shingle beaches and sand beaches in Lancashire.'*

Figure 1.9 Distinguishing between aims, questions and hypotheses.

Identifying personal and project risk

At the very start it is essential to establish that the focus for the fieldwork and research is feasible and safe. Some hypotheses may be impossible or unwise to test, due to:
• practical problems of measurement (for example, it may be difficult or dangerous to study rates of erosion or mass movement on some river banks or coastal cliffs)
• inaccessibility (for example, research locations on private property)
• lack of available secondary data (for example, some historic river and catchment data from the National Rivers Flow Archive cannot be easily and freely accessed without special permissions; some research publications may be difficult to get hold of without visiting a university library)
• lack of data to support findings in temporal studies looking at change over time or rates.

Using the national Census is another key area of fieldwork research which is not free of project risk. Practical problems can also arise as a result of boundary changes to the small spatial units used to create area output data about local populations. In 2001, for example, the old enumeration districts for small areas were replaced by a series of new output areas. This resulting lack of comparable spatial data has made it harder to investigate population changes over time in some settlements.

Using geographical concepts in your enquiry goals

The A level geography specifications make particular reference to specialised geographical concepts. There are fourteen of these: causality, systems, equilibrium, feedback, inequality, representation, identity, globalisation, interdependence, mitigation and adaptation, sustainability, risk, resilience and thresholds.

These key words feature prominently in the work of university geographers. You will also see the same terminology used by more sophisticated newspapers and magazines. Although some of the concepts have greater affinity with either physical or human geography, most of them matter for both subject areas. Take the example of **thresholds**, for instance. Thresholds in physical systems can be (critical) tipping points after which the system shifts radically – and potentially irreversibly – into a different **equilibrium state**. But the same idea is also used in human geography: for example, there may be a threshold population level for a region which, if it is exceeded, triggers a critical change in environmental conditions.

Top Tip
Using technical documents
These can include complicated graphics, tables and data. Use extracts in your investigation if the information genuinely supports what you are doing. But beware of using hard-to-understand and potentially irrelevant information that is not directly linked to the purpose or focus of your enquiry.

Top Tip
Using specialised concepts
Inclusion of specialised concepts linked to fieldwork could add an extra dimension or layer of complexity that pays dividends in terms of trying to make you work both more relevant and sophisticated. See Figure 1.10 for examples.

You will be expected to demonstrate a sound understanding of the threshold idea, along with the thirteen other specialised concepts, in varying contexts through your course. Why not try to make use of one or more of these concepts in your enquiry aims, questions or hypotheses? Using them in an introduction or conclusion is equally valuable. Figure 1.10 suggests some ways in which this could be done.

Figure 1.10 Examples of specialised concepts and possible individual investigation opportunities.

Concept	Definition	Examples of individual investigation opportunities
Resilience	The capacity of a system to experience shocks, while retaining essentially the same function, structure, feedbacks and identity.	• Flood risk and community resilience. • Economy of a town and its resilience against economic recession. • Ecosystem resilience.
System	Systems thinking is the process of understanding how connected things (parts) influence one another within a complete entity or larger network.	• Inputs, outputs and stores within a local hydrological sub-catchment. • Economy of an urban centre as a system. • Understanding carbon flows in a woodland ecosystem.
Place identity	Place identity describes the real or perceived qualities in how somewhere appears to people; it affects how we connect with neighbourhoods and locales. It is about belonging, meaning and attachment to places at a very personalised level.	• Place identity as perceived by tourists. • The identity of rural places and the identity of urban places. • Connections to place for people of different ages or cultures.

Summarising why planning matters

Designing a practical and workable investigation, which follows a clear route to enquiry, is likely to pay dividends. A well-conceived approach brings several benefits. It:
- stimulates curiosity and allows you to challenge concepts, models, theories and beliefs
- it facilitates the development of meaningful and multifaceted questions which do not have simple 'yes' or 'no' answers
- it allows a way of thinking which is often more reflective and that can help with understanding the complexity of 'messy' real-world geography.

This chapter was the starting point for the individual investigation. Subsequent chapters in this book will help you build and develop the breadth of skills and competencies required in order to undertake and complete a high-quality piece of investigative work.

References

- Roberts, M. (2013), *Geography Through Enquiry*. Geographical Association.
- DfE GCE AS and A level subject content for geography. Available at: https://www.gov.uk/government/uploads/system/uploads/attachment_data/file/3888 57/GCE_AS_and_A_level_subject_content_for_geography.pdf
- Fieldwork methodology: Barcelona Field Studies. Available at: http://geographyfieldwork.com/FieldworkMethodology.htm
- Geographical Enquiry covered by the Field Studies Council (FSC). Available at: https://www.gov.uk/government/uploads/system/uploads/attachment_data/file/ 388857/GCE_AS_and_A_level_subject_content_for_geography.pdf
- The inductive approach to fieldwork. Available at: http://research-methodology.net/research-methodology
- The deductive approach to fieldwork. Available at: http://research-methodology.net/research-methodology

(all websites last accessed Feb 2018)

2 Data collection and analysis

Objectives

- *Understand how sampling is used to generate quality data in both physical and human geography, including the strengths and weaknesses of particular sampling methods.*

- *Understand key data collection methods, in particular, human geography techniques.*

- *Recognise the value of word cloud analysis of secondary data.*

Introducing sampling

You cannot pick up all the stones on a beach. Nor can you interview every resident of a large town. On the other hand, would measurement of just one stone or an interview with a single person be sufficient data to collect? If you calculated the infiltration rate at a single site in a drainage basin, would it be acceptable to use that information as a representative measure of the river catchment as a whole? Common sense already tells us the answer is no.

Between the two extremes lies a carefully selected set of measurements called a **sample**. A selection of data is collected from the entire *population* of things or people you could potentially survey. In the examples used above, the populations would be:
- all the stones found along a section of beach
- every person who lives in a town
- every possible survey point in a drainage basin.

Over to you
Devise a sampling strategy to find out what are the typical views of students at your school about an issue such as lowering the voting age. How many people would you need to sample? Would the survey need to be stratified to include representatives of different year groups or genders?

Sample size and data variability

The next logical thing to consider is: 'How large does my sample need to be?' The size of your sample depends on the answers to a series of questions shown in Figure 2.1.

1. How many measurements are needed to draw a graph or conduct a statistical test?

2. How variable are the data?

3. How much time do I have?

4. What equipment and other resources are available?

Figure 2.1 Deciding on the size of a sample needs to be planned carefully because it affects the reliability of any conclusions which are reached later.
Source: David Holmes

Figure 2.2 Stone measurements and the running mean stone size for two different river survey sites

Stone number	Location A 1° axis length cm	Location A Running mean/cm	Location B 1° axis length/cm	Location B Running mean/cm
1	8.2	8.2	1.8	1.8
2	0.7	4.5	7.0	4.4
3	6.0	5.0	1.0	3.3
4	1.5	4.1	2.1	3.0
5	2.5	3.8	1.1	2.6
6	9.0	4.7	8.0	3.5
7	5.7	4.8	2.8	3.4
8	3.1	4.6	14.7	14.7
9	6.5	4.8	2.6	4.6
10	8.5	5.2	12.4	5.4
11	2.0	4.9	3.4	5.2
12	3.0	4.7	16.1	6.1
13	9.8	5.1	0.2	5.6
14	6.0	5.2	3.3	5.5
15	4.7	5.1	3.2	5.3
16	9.9	5.4	4.2	5.2
17	10.8	5.8	0.5	5.0
18	4.8	5.7	13.0	5.4
19	1.7	5.5	5.0	5.4
20	6.3	5.5	0.4	5.1
21	1.1	5.3	5.0	5.1
22	0.4	5.1	6.0	5.2
23	4.8	5.1	0.3	5.0
24	0.6	4.9	1.5	4.8
25	5.8	4.9	2.2	4.7
26	9.4	5.1	14.6	5.1
27	10.3	5.3	16.1	5.5
28	7.5	5.4	11.6	5.7
29	10.2	5.5	4.8	5.7
30	1.8	5.4	1.1	5.5
31	10.6	5.6	5.8	5.5
32	1.9	5.5	5.3	5.5
33	1.9	5.4	3.0	5.5
34	2.5	5.3	1.9	5.4
35	8.5	5.4	5.9	5.4
36	1.1	5.3	3.9	5.4
37	5.8	5.3	3.9	5.3
38	10.4	5.4	16.5	5.6
39	1.4	5.3	12.7	5.8
40	1.9	5.2	15.5	6.0
41	5.2	5.2	1.7	5.9
42	8.4	5.3	15.4	6.1
43	0.5	5.2	4.2	6.1
44	2.6	5.1	9.8	6.2
45	6.0	5.1	7.4	6.2
46	7.8	5.2	16.0	6.4
47	2.1	5.1	15.8	6.6
48	5.8	5.1	2.5	6.5
49	9.6	5.2	9.3	6.6
50	2.0	5.2	3.2	6.5

With respect to the *variability* of data, there is one basic and important rule to follow: the more variable your measurements are, the larger the sample you should aim for. For instance, if the first ten stones sampled from a glacial deposit are all spherical with a diameter of approximately 5.2 cm, then it might seem reasonable not to take any more measurements. Sediments in natural systems often come in all sorts of shapes and sizes, however. As a result, a larger sample than ten will be needed. But how much larger?

It's often difficult to know how many measurements you will need to make before you start sampling. Once you have started collecting data, you can generate a **cumulative mean** (or running mean) value. This helps you to see how the mean 'stabilises' as your data set gets bigger. Figures 2.2 and 2.3 illustrate how this works in practice for a sediment survey carried out at two river sites.

At Location A, the running mean has stabilised after about 30 measurements. This suggests a sample of 30 stones is a sufficiently large sample for that site.

The data from Location B are more variable. The running mean takes longer to stabilise. A sample of 50 measurements would be needed here in order to gain a reliable picture of what is going on. If your investigation involved making a comparison of the mean sediment size found at the two sites, then it would be best to carry out a sample of the same number of stones at each site. Fifty measurements should therefore be made at each location.

Using a running mean is a simple, effective and useful way of demonstrating the suitability of your sample size. Some researchers will carry out a **pilot survey** at a single site ahead of carrying out the rest of their research. Use of the running mean at the pilot site helps them to decide how much data they will collect when carrying out the full investigation.

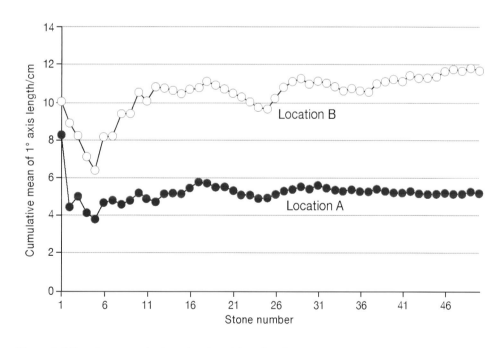

Figure 2.3 Running mean for Location A and Location B.

Establishing the minimum number of sample measurements

Before you start sampling, give careful consideration to the data analysis techniques which you anticipate using eventually. Some basic ideas that you must think about are shown in Figure 2.4.

The running mean is a useful indicator of the desirable sample size but there are plenty of other things to consider. One key question is: are your data normally distributed? The answer is 'yes' if your data are spread symmetrically around the median (middle) value and would produce a bell-shaped graph. A survey of grass height in a drylands environment is likely to show a **normal distribution**. For instance, most grasses will be medium-sized, with fewer very short or very tall grasses. In contrast, many sediment size distributions do not show a normal distribution. Instead, the distribution is often **skewed**: a large number of very small particles will be found with relatively fewer medium and large-sized stones.

Sometimes the effect you are looking at is weak, subtle or unclear, for example a relatively small difference between two averages (means or medians) or a weak correlation between two variables. Then you will need more measurements in your samples than you would if the effect was stronger (for example, a big difference between averages or a stronger correlation).

	Research question focus				
	Am I investigating the **difference between two or more populations**?		Am I looking for a **correlation between two phenomena** (found in a number of different locations)?		Am I investigating the '**goodness of fit**' (between observed and expected values) for samples of different populations?
Are your data normally distributed?	No	Yes	No	Yes	N/A
Appropriate statistical tests to apply	Median, range and interquartile range, Mann Whitney U-test	Mean, standard deviation and confidence limits, Student's t-test	Spearman's rank correlation	Pearson product-moment correlation	Chi-squared test
Suggested minimum sample size	8–15 measurements (replicates) in each data set	15–50 measurements (replicates) in each data set	12–15 pairs of data	12–15 pairs of data	None of the (predicted) test values should be less than 5
Appropriate graphs to draw	Box and whisker plots	Bar charts of means with standard deviation or confidence limits	Scattergraphs	Scattergraphs	Bar or pie charts of the observed (recorded) sample data

Time, resources, equipment, etc. will limit how much sampling you can do. You need to carefully plan the study to make sure that you get an opportunity to measure at least the minimum number of samples (see Figure 2.4).

Figure 2.4 Questions to ask when establishing an ideal sample size.

It's quite likely that you will only be able to allocate a certain amount of time to collect your data. You will not know how long it is going to take to collect all the data unless you do a small pilot study to check how long it takes to collect **one** (complete) set of data. That could be measuring the gradient of a cliff, or finding and asking one person to fill in a questionnaire or measuring the infiltration rate at one location. In terms of quality, this may need to be done at least eight to fifteen times at each of two sites.

So do it once and check:

- How long it takes to collect *each* sample? (let's say each sample takes 20 minutes).
- Work out how much time you can allow to collect all the measurements (perhaps you only have 6 hours to collect your data).
- Does that give you enough time to achieve the minimum number of samples needed in the time you've set aside to collect data? (If you could do 18 samples in 6 hours that means you could do at least 9 in each of two sites.)

If you do not think you have enough time then change your methods; make things simpler to allow time to collect more measurements. Saying in your write-up that you ran out of time to collect the data is something you will want to avoid.

Representative and reliable sampling methods

Sampling is about trying to be sure that the measurements taken are representative of the entire population (which is often made up of a large number of unmeasured things alongside a smaller number of measured things). Unfortunately, it's all too easy to collect data and information in a way that introduces **bias** and therefore a degree of unreliability to the sample.

Sampling strategies are systems that reduce this risk. There are three important and widely-used strategies: these are the random, stratified and systematic sampling methods. Alternative techniques exist which can also be used if the situation demands it, such as snowball sampling.

Random sampling

Random sampling is when each possible sampling unit (an individual, object or event within your **sampling population**) has exactly the same chance of being sampled as any other.

Picking numbers from a hat is a classic example of a random sample (provided each number is returned to the hat after being picked out). But instead of a hat, researchers can choose to use a table of random numbers or a random number generator to assist their enquiry (a random number app can be added easily to a smartphone).

To start with, you need to define exactly what your sampling population is. For example, it could be all of the vegetation growing on a sports pitch. When studying vegetation, a **quadrat** is often used. This is often a metre-square frame which is placed on the ground and the number of species or average height of vegetation in the quadrat is recorded. There are different types of quadrat, the choice of which depends on the size and variation of what is being measured. For example, gridded quadrats can help in finding percentage cover or percentage frequency values.

Let us assume that a student wants to carry out a survey of ten sample sites on the pitch. Where should their locations be? One random method involves drawing a map of the pitch and adding grid squares (just like on an Ordnance Survey map). The random number app on your smartphone can then be used to generate ten grid references. Locate each point on the real pitch and drop your quadrat there (though try not to introduce bias at the last minute by placing it in a way which deliberately covers or avoids particular species or ground features).

The use of large tape measures can help you to identify the exact coordinates your random number generator has told you to visit (Figure 2.5).

The use of randomly-selected grid squares and coordinates can be justified as an appropriate technique when carrying out surveys in urban areas. There is a tendency among students to select study areas based purely on factors such as familiarity, ease of

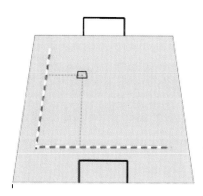

Figure 2.5 Locating a randomly-generated grid coordinate with the aid of two tape measures.

access and perceptions of comfort or even safety. While these are all important considerations, it's easy to see how a biased selection of sampling points could lead to skewed results. You might end up interviewing only high-income individuals living in high-class residential areas, for instance, instead of sampling a more diverse range of people and attitudes.

Sometimes restrictions need to be introduced when defining your sampling population in accordance with your research question(s):

1   One student develops a questionnaire investigating the views of young people in relation to a new shopping centre. He may decide only to interview young people aged 10–20 years. This subset of the town's population is now defined as the investigation's sampling population.
2   Another student carries out a survey of chalk pebbles on a beach where many different types of rock can be found. The chalk subset of the beach's sediment store has become this investigation's sampling population.

Actually randomising the selection of people or pebbles from within either of these sampling populations must now be carefully considered. One approach might be to generate a list of random numbers. Next, arrange them in order and use these numbers to select your people or pebbles. For instance, you might hand your questionnaire to the 3rd, 7th, 8th and 28th person who walks past you. Or you could measure the 5th, 9th, 30th and 192nd pebble along a **transect** that you create on the beach.

Stratified random sampling

Stratified random sampling is sampling which is adjusted to take into account important features and characteristics which may divide the population being studied.

If you have ever watched the National Lottery draw, you will know that sometimes all the balls are the same colour. The result of this random selection process can be six green balls numbered 32, 33, 34, 35, 37 and 39 for instance (which hardly seems representative). Similarly, a random sample of ten people in a village could result in only pensioners being chosen, while working and young people are excluded entirely. How then do you ensure that you do not introduce bias into your results by either over-sampling one age group or missing another entirely?

Similar problems can arise when using random sampling methods in physical geography. A student is investigating the infiltration rate of soil in a river catchment, for instance. She surveys a small number of randomly selected locations. However, all of the random grid coordinates she generates – by chance – take her to locations with woodland and good drainage). The survey misses out entirely large portions of the catchment where grassland with poorer drainage is present. As a result, the survey has a biased outcome and represents the catchment as a whole very poorly.

One possible solution in both cases would be to carry out a modified form of random sampling that allocates samples according to important variations which exist within the sampling population.

1   Census data show that 40 per cent of people in the village are retired. Therefore, the student could quite reasonably decide to interview four pensioners (chosen at random) and six working-age or young people (also chosen at random).
2   The student carrying out the infiltration study could use a vegetation map to help stratify her sample. Figure 2.6 shows the approximate area of the catchment covered by short calcareous grassland is about 45 per cent, while about the same amount is covered by short acidic grassland with just 10 per cent woodland. Proportionately, a stratified sample of 20 measurements would involve nine values recorded in short acidic grassland, another nine in short calcareous grassland and just two in woodland.

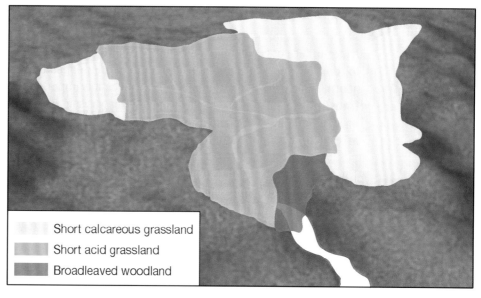

Figure 2.6 A stratifed random sampling method could be applied in order to ensure a survey is properly representative of the different proportions of grasslands and woodland found here.

Legend:
- Short calcareous grassland
- Short acid grassland
- Broadleaved woodland

Systematic sampling

Systematic sampling is sampling which investigates an expected change as we move from one location to another, or sampling carried out when there is a practical need to take regular measurements along a transect (line).

Sampling in these situations is often done systematically, either at fixed distances along a transect or according to positions fixed by some other factor. For instance, readings might be taken at fixed morphological points across a drylands dune system, including each major ridge, hollow or slack which is encountered. An urban transect might incorporate a traffic count at each road which is encountered. These data can be analysed subsequently by testing for a statistical correlation between linked measurements recorded at each site.

Snowball sampling

Snowball sampling is a method used in human geography when the details of the sampling population are unclear and a referral system is needed.

A student carrying out an investigation into global systems wants to interview illegal migrants living in the UK. Another student looking at places needs to talk to graffiti artists. In both cases there is a problem: there are no official records or sampling frames available to select interviewees from. However, if one person can be found to talk to, then that individual may be able to provide the contact for other migrants or artists who could be prepared to help. You can see why this method is called 'snowball sampling'. One risk associated with this sampling system is that it is hard to tell how representative the data are of the sampling population (most of whom remain unknown).

Collecting different types of data

Chapter 1, page 11 provided a brief introduction to primary, secondary, quantitative and qualitative data categories. You may end up using all four types in your own independent investigation.

Secondary data are widely perceived as information that has been collected and presented and/or analysed previously by other people. It may be available in the form of maps, Census data or academic papers, for instance. In some cases, secondary data is available in a 'raw' quantitative form which you can analyse yourself alongside your primary information. You might conduct a random sample of names listed in the 1901 Census to find out what the average age of a place's population used to be. Indeed, an investigation of demographic change over time could legitimately make greater use of secondary data than primary data provided you can demonstrate you are working creatively with a data set as you set about answering your research question(s).

Over to you

Which of the data sources in Figure 2.7 are primary data and which are secondary data?

19

Question 1 – How often have you eaten at this café?	Question 2 – Are you a local person or a visitor to this city?				Row total
	Local	Expected value	Outside	Expected value	
It's my first time	1	18	34	17	35
About once a year	3	12	21	12	24
A few times a year	21	14	6	13	27
Once a month	42	26	10	26	52
Once a week	13	11	8	10	21
Column total	80		79		159

Figure 2.8 Questionnaire data which have been analysed to carry out a Chi-squared statistical test.

You can find a Chi-squared contingency table online.

Details of how to access online resources are on page 3.

Analysing questionnaire data

Questionnaires generate frequency data that may suit statistical analysis using the Chi-squared (χ^2) test. An example of how you might carry out the analysis of linked data from two questions is shown in the box below. Here, a researcher wants to know whether there is significant difference in the frequency with which local people use a tourist café when compared with visitors from outside the area (the null hypothesis used would be that there is no difference in behaviour).

The 'expected value' in each case is the frequency we would expect if visitors and local people behaved in the same way. It is calculated using the formula: (row total x column total) ÷ grand total.

The Chi-squared test uses the formula $\chi^2 = \Sigma(O-E)^2/E$.

In this case, it generates a result of 74, which shows there is a very significant difference in the behaviour of the two groups. An alternative way of viewing the result is to say it shows a strong association between where respondents come from and how frequently they visit. A statistical conclusion does not include any geographical explanation and as geographers you will need to explore reasons for the statistical conclusion.

As with any frequency data, a chart can provide a graphical summary of the data (Figure 2.9).

Figure 2.9 A graphical summary of the observed data.

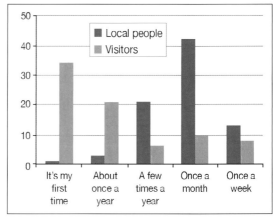

You can carry out this Chi-squared procedure yourself in order to practise your quantitative skills. You will need to use a good statistics guide and Chi-squared contingency table.

Conducting ethnographic research

Ethnography is the study of people and places. It is an observational approach to data collection that allows us to explore the interactions between individuals and groups of people and places. If you sit on a town centre bench and watch the world go by, geographical questions may present themselves:
- Are different shops attracting different age groups?
- Are most shoppers in groups or alone?
- How much time are people spending here?

Having observed certain things, you can start thinking about how best to record these phenomena. You could decide to systematically select to interview every tenth person or group of people to pass by. You might ask them to draw a map showing their movement through the area and the shops they visit (Figure 2.10). You may additionally stratify the

Figure 2.10 The paths taken by a sample of shoppers (the interviewer can draw these lines themselves if you provide a tablet or large smartphone for them to use

Source: www.scribblemaps.com

Figure 2.11 Annotations added to a photograph of Chester town centre.

Source: http://wcnwchamber.org.uk

- Pedestrianised road with some parked cars. Separated from shops on either side of the road by parked cars and bollards.
- Cobbled road surface is uneven. Very few people over 45 walking in this area. Appealing more to young couples with children and 'off-road' pushchairs, and individual men.
- Least densely-used area with most space and fewest pedestrians, allowing ease of movement for those wishing to avoid distractions of shops or pass through the area quickly. Highest speed of pedestrian movement in this area.

- Pavement area, protected by bollards and adjacent to hotel.
- Predominantly older pedestrians – over-55s, often in couples. No shops on this side of the road so pedestrians 'passing through'.
- Walking surface paved with flat slabs creating a smooth walking surface, perhaps more appealing to older visitors due to increased chance of tripping on cobbled road section.

- Shop frontages, same paved slab surface as other side of the road, protected by bollards in places.
- Densely-used area and slowest speed of pedestrian movement.
- Primarily under-45s, majority are young couples and women in pairs.
- Shopping and window-shopping area – narrow walkway keeps people in this area close to windows to maximise potential of window displays to engage the interest of pedestrians.

survey to include sub-groups of older and younger people in an effort to make your sample representative of all users of urban space.

Videos are useful for recording temporal changes (perhaps the area is used differently at varying times of the day) and there could be public access webcams you can extract data from. You can annotate your own photographs with your thoughts and impressions of a place (Figure 2.11). There are smartphone apps which assist with this.

Also, think about where you will be when you observe this place. If you want to record movements of particular individuals then you ought to be operating at street level. If you are more interested in recording broader flows of the crowd then an elevated viewpoint may help you see patterns more clearly.

Over to you
Can you find an official document or research paper relating to your own investigation which is suitable for word cloud analysis? Give it a go!

Collecting and analysing documents

One final data collection idea for you to think about is the way in which you make use of secondary data such as tourist brochures or environmental reports. Wordle is an online tool which creates a visual representation of text called a word cloud. This is created by counting each time a word appears, and scaling the word proportionally. A word with a high frequency of use is given a large text (font) size, whereas a low frequency is shown by a smaller text size. Word clouds make it possible to easily identify any recurring themes embedded within the text.

It can be a very useful way of uncovering important issues relating to the place where you plan to carry out your investigation. Figure 2.12 shows a word cloud created using Wordle. It analyses the frequency with which words have been used in a tourist website promoting the town of Ludlow. It is immediately apparent that food, drink and festivals play a prominent role in the place making process for Ludlow. Figure 2.13 shows how a word cloud can also reveal themes for further study in a physical geography investigation. Flood management issues have been analysed to reveal the top 40 keywords. Could any of these serve as key foci for an enquiry question?

Figure 2.12 Word cloud created using text from the tourist website for Ludlow.
Source: www.ludlow.org.uk

Figure 2.13 Word cloud created using a flood management overview provided at *The British Geographer* website.

References

- The Robert Wood Johnson Foundation has sponsored the Qualitative Research Guidelines Project to develop a website that will be useful for people developing, evaluating and engaging in qualitative research projects. Available at: http://www.qualres.org

- Wordle website: www.wordle.net

(Last accessed Feb 2018)

3 Using GIS in your investigation

Objectives

- *Understand the varied ways in which Geographical Information Systems (GIS) data can support your individual investigation.*

- *Understand the basic 'tricks of the trade' that will help get you started using GIS.*

- *Understand the value of GIS for each stage of the investigation – from carrying out background research to conducting data analysis.*

Using locational data to ask geographical questions

A commonly quoted statistic claims that: '80% of all data are geographic'. Whether that figure is roughly accurate or a complete myth is up for debate. It is, however, true to say that the data we encounter in our everyday lives often contain some sort of locational aspect. Just look at today's news headlines: all the events you read about will have happened in particular places.

Locational information is the bread and butter of geographers. We use it to build a picture of people and processes working within the landscapes we study. The contexts can vary from rural to urban, coastal to mountain, or densely populated to wild and remote. Whatever the setting, it is usual to begin the investigation with a data set which includes a *locational* element.

Figure 3.1 An extract from a larger table containing the location of bus stops in Burton on Trent. **Source**: National Public Transport Access Nodes, Department of Transport – Open Government Licence

Common Name	Town	Longitude	Latitude
The Beacon Hotel	Burton upon Trent	-1.652647616	52.83073792
The Beacon Hotel	Burton upon Trent	-1.653340063	52.8313872
Kitling Greaves Lane	Burton upon Trent	-1.649550995	52.82635981
Kitling Greaves Lane	Burton upon Trent	-1.648768044	52.82590801
Merlin Crescent	Burton upon Trent	-1.6671831	52.79132355
Beaufort Road Top	Burton upon Trent	-1.593995412	52.8013261

Figure 3.2 Using GIS to map the bus stops (purple dots) will prompt us to start asking geographical questions. **Source:** National Public Transport Access Nodes, Department of Transport – map prepared using ArcGIS Online

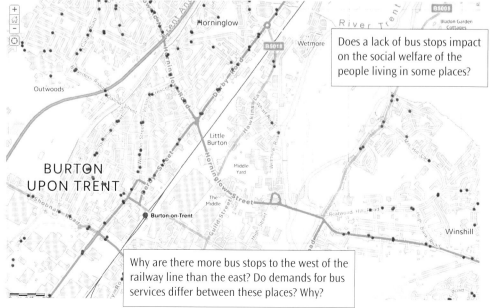

Does a lack of bus stops impact on the social welfare of the people living in some places?

Why are there more bus stops to the west of the railway line than the east? Do demands for bus services differ between these places? Why?

25

Figure 3.1 shows a possible starting point for someone who is undertaking a study of transport networks in their home neighbourhood. In table form, the information has little value. However, we can visualise actual distances and patterns as soon as the locational elements (longitude and latitude) of the bus stops have been mapped (Figure 3.2). We can also start formulating hypotheses or asking geographical questions about what we see.

At this point we might decide we need to know more. How large an area does a bus stop serve? This might be influenced by how far people are prepared to walk to get to the nearest bus stop (this may differ for residents of rural and urban areas). For the next step of our GIS-led investigation, let's enquire into which areas are located no more than five minutes away from a bus stop (Figure 3.3).

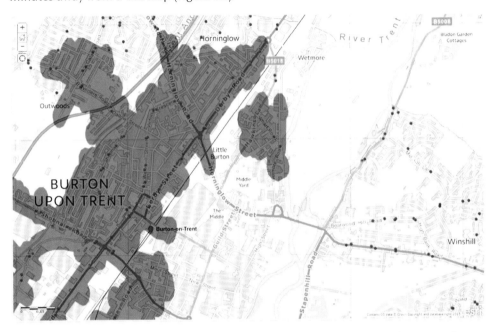

Figure 3.3 The purple shading indicates streets and places within 'walkable' reach (five minutes) of a bus stop. **Source:** National Public Transport Access Nodes, Department of Transport – map prepared using ArcGIS Online

A new hypothesis springs to mind: perhaps western areas lack bus stops because of a higher rate of car ownership there? If fewer people need to use buses then the operator may run a reduced service. Therefore, our next step is to use UK Census data showing car ownership in Burton Upon Trent. Figure 3.4 shows this information now added to our map. Do the new data support our hypothesis?

Figure 3.4 The bus stops and 'walkable' areas have been overlain on a **choropleth** map showing levels of car ownership: darker blue indicates more cars. **Source:** National Public Transport Access Nodes, Department of Transport and ONS Census 2011 – map prepared using ArcGIS Online

By thinking and working spatially, we have been able to fully explore a series of interesting geographical questions and hypotheses.

Geospatial technologies and geographic data

The tools for collecting, storing, processing and communicating data have evolved over time. In recent years, computers have revolutionised how spatial data is handled. Today, we can collect, display and share vast quantities of data virtually instantaneously.

Geospatial technology (Figure 3.5) has become a great asset for researchers who want to collect, manage and communicate data. It can support geography students through every stage of the enquiry process. In the wider world, 'hidden' geospatial technologies now support and drive many businesses.

Figure 3.5 The language of geospatial technology.

Geospatial technology	Software and hardware used to visualise, measure and analyse data that is associated with geographic locations. This umbrella term includes all the elements shown below.
GPS	*A space-based navigation system that provides location and time information anywhere on Earth.* Satellites orbiting the Earth send out signals which, with the use of a GPS (global positioning system) receiver, can be used to accurately determine a location. Dedicated GPS devices are available, but the chances are that you already have one in your smartphone! Using GPS, accurate locational data can be accessed via wifi or mobile networks.
Geotagging	*Attaching a location (latitude and longitude) to a file so that it can be located on a map.* The location of each bus stop in Figure 3.2 was most likely captured using GPS. The GPS in your smart phone can be used to geotag photographs. Some social media sites like Facebook encourage you to geotag your images.
Remote sensing	*Collecting data from afar.* This includes satellite or aerial photography, radar and a technology called Lidar. Global data at almost any resolution can be gathered from space. For small areas, where high resolution images are needed, aeroplanes and drones are used. Remote sensing images can be an important form of secondary data.
Digital mapping	Remotely-sensed data are increasingly used in the production of maps. Most internet mapping sites make use of remotely-sensed imagery. Modern digital mapping techniques 'trace' features over ground images. These are then 'ground-truthed' to ensure that what is on the map reflects properly what is on the ground.
GIS (Geographical Information Systems)	*Software designed to capture, store, manipulate, analyse, manage and present all types of spatial data.* These technological systems bring together and use many different geospatial elements by combining layers of mapping, remotely-sensed data and geolocated data (both primary and secondary) to show what is happening in a place.

Top Tip
Using GIS to find geographic patterns
By consulting remotely-sensed data and digital maps, you may identify important geographic patterns or features prior to designing a strategy which aims to sample 'real' data up close and in the field.

Understanding the basics of GIS

A range of GIS options exist. Your own choice will depend on a number of factors, including availability, accessibility and cost. Many organisations that hold data (such as the Environment Agency) use web-based GIS to make sure this information becomes available easily to the public online. Some platforms, including Google Earth, allow you to add digital layers to the maps provided using your own data. More sophisticated platforms, such as ArcGIS, let you merge your data with that of other people.

All Geographical Information Systems (GIS) use the same basic building blocks. Figure 3.6 provides a guide to the essential elements of GIS.

Location	All information in GIS must be tied to a geographical location. Most use latitudinal and longitudinal data but you may also work with post codes or Ordnance Survey grid references (some websites will convert locational data for you). The type of data you collect will impact on the type of locational information you decide to record. When locating data you can choose to work with points, lines or polygons.
Point	A single location defined by one pair of coordinates (e.g. locations of individual trees, pedestrian count points, sites of reported crimes or the point where a bus stop is found).
Line	A series of points joined in order to create a line (e.g. the route taken by a shopper across a town, a stretch of road showing traffic congestion or the path followed by a river or field boundary).
Polygon (shape)	A series of coordinates which have been joined together producing a closed shape. (e.g. an area of woodland, a building's footprint, a local government ward or Census output area).
Attribute	In GIS, some further information is recorded about every location (point, line or polygon). These extra attributes could consist of text, numerical data or associated photographs. In our example of bus stops on page 27, 'Common Name' and 'Town' are text attributes which have been recorded alongside the location (latitude and longitude).
Layer	GIS works by allowing us to build up multiple layers of information. By viewing these together, we can see spatial patterns and relationships between variables.

Any primary data you input into GIS will be in point, line or polygon form. These are known collectively as **vector data.** Some secondary data used in GIS has a different format and is called **raster data** (Figure 3.7).

Figure 3.6 The basic elements of all GIS.

Figure 3.7 Vector and raster describe the world in different levels of detail.

Vector data are coordinate-based locations (with a collection of attributes attached to every place or location).

Raster data represent the world by dividing it into grid squares.

The locations of individual trees are shown as points. In GIS, each point may have attributes attached, such as species or height.

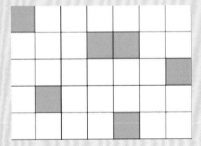

On this map, trees are present in the coloured grid squares (pixels). But we cannot tell how many trees are in each pixel/square.

A series of points (coordinate-based locations) have been joined (like 'dot-to-dot'). The smoothness of the line depends on how many points have been mapped.

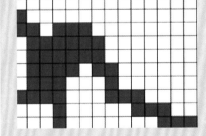

Here, the squares are blue if the river passes through that pixel. We have no way of knowing how much of each square is filled with water, or how wide the river is.

Areas of different land use (urban, rural, farmland) are mapped using polygons. The boundaries reflect real-life edges of areas formed by features such as hedges or fences.

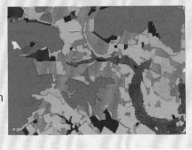

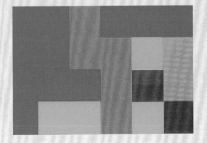

Land use is displayed in a series of 1km x 1km pixels. The colour shows the dominant land use within the pixel (though it may not be the only use).

Top Tip
How detailed
should my maps
be?
If you use raster data, think carefully about what resolution to use. 1km x 1km squares are fine if you are showing a large river catchment like the Severn or Thames. But you will need more detail if looking at a small upland stream.

Using GIS to help you get started

There are many different routes when starting an investigation. You might begin by choosing the place where you want to work and think of a topic later. Or you may choose the topic (e.g. a river study) ahead of finding a suitable case area. However you begin, some preliminary research will help you generate a well-informed research question. Most people draw on geospatial information and GIS to help them.

The early stages of your decision making will most likely follow one of two pathways:

1 All your class are being led by the teachers to the same place as part of a group fieldtrip. You fall into the 'I know for sure where my investigation will be based' category.

2 You have a strong desire to investigate independently a particular topic such as sea level change. You fall into the 'I know what I want to study, but not where' category.

Either starting point requires some 'contextualising research' before questions or hypotheses are generated. Figure 3.8 suggests a route this early research may follow.

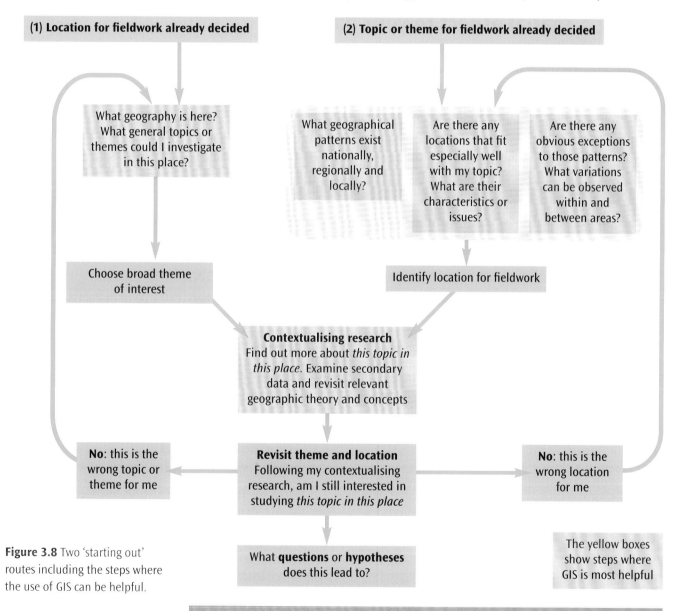

Figure 3.8 Two 'starting out' routes including the steps where the use of GIS can be helpful.

Data collection using GIS

When it comes to carrying out your actual fieldwork, GIS can be a big help. You may have access to GIS packages which will allow you to collect data using GIS directly from the field. Alternatively, you could use a smartphone or tablet to collect your data into a spreadsheet. This could then be loaded into your GIS software for data presentation and analysis. Doing this saves time, thereby allowing you to survey a wider area or collect a larger data sample. It also eliminates the tedious process of recording data by hand before transcribing it into a computer. A 'pilot' visit to the fieldwork site prior to the main visit is a good opportunity to try out different data collection techniques.

Different types of data

GIS categorises all attribute data into one of four types. How you handle and process data is dependent on the data type you use. The data may come from counts, measurements, the application of an index, a questionnaire (with either open or closed questions), field notes, or images such as field sketches and annotated photos.

Adding a spatial aspect to your data

Adding a spatial aspect to data points, areas or polygons (see page 28) means using a recording system that will additionally describe the location of your information. It is therefore important to check that the GIS or mapping package you will use can do this. Figure 3.9 shows different locational systems you might use. Some smartphone apps let you add information to geolocated points. Or you can enable geotagging on your smartphone camera (this captures the latitude and longitude of any photos you take). By taking these sensible steps you can utilise GIS later in your data presentation and analysis.

**Top Tip
Be selective with the GIS data you collect**

All types of data have their uses, but reflect carefully on what will be most valuable for your investigation. Firstly, ask yourself: *which data will help me answer my questions and which will not?* It helps to make a list of all of the data types you want to collect and have a **rationale** for each of them.

Figure 3.9 Locational systems and possible uses.

Location system	When to use it	Things to consider
Provide latitude and longitude for each data collection point	When you collect data at a fixed point	• describes the location of any point globally • works with all digital mapping and GIS systems • a GPS app will identify the latitude and longitude of any data collection points.
Attach the OS grid reference to a measurement site	When you collect data at a fixed point	• describes the location of any point in the UK • a GPS app or OS map will help you identify the grid reference for any location • most GIS systems do not use OS grid references.
Record the postcode of a street or local area	When you collect data about a street or small local area	• postcode information is easy to find: ask almost anyone their postcode and they could tell you! • most GIS and digital mapping systems use postcodes • good to use with questionnaires when you want to know where someone lives • cannot be used to locate a single dwelling.
Show the Census Output Area (an area of around 125 households)	When you collect data about a street or small local area	• allows you to cross-reference your findings with a mass of secondary data • not widely known about: most people do not know what Census output area they live in.

**Top Tip
Do not overcomplicate graphics**

ICT can be a great help when it comes to presenting your data. Both spreadsheets and GIS help geographers to display their data quickly and easily. Think critically about whether the graphs and maps you create using software help communicate your data clearly. The same principle applies to maps made using GIS. It has become relatively easy to create complicated maps. Remember that the first principle of good cartography is that a map should make navigation clearer and trends and patterns easier to interpret.

Data presentation and analysis using GIS

Over to you

Do GIS images feature in any of your course textbooks? Analyse the techniques that have been used: for example do they show vector or raster data?

Presenting categorical data

Imagine you have completed a land use survey within a river catchment. You have identified areas with the same land use and are now ready to assign a colour to each category. It makes sense to choose colours that help the reader interpret the map quickly. In Figure 3.10, shades of green have been used to represent grassland and woodland. Freshwater is blue and built-up areas are black.

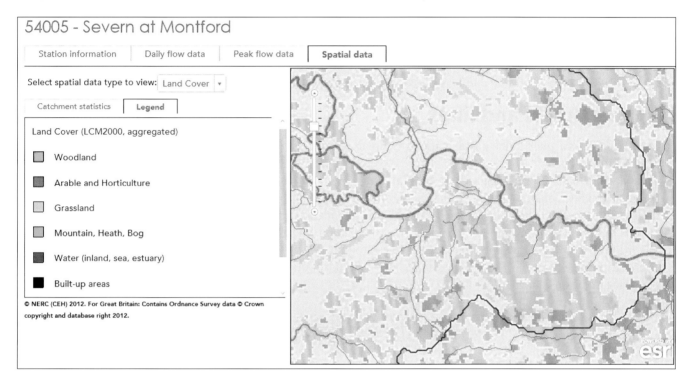

Figure 3.10 A thematic map showing land cover within part of the Upper Severn catchment.
Source: National River Flow Archive

Using choropleth maps

Choropleth maps use a colour ramp. This is a sliding scale of colour which corresponds with changing data values. Choropleth maps are widely used in atlases to show variations in temperature, population density and many other geographic features and patterns. To use a choropleth map correctly, we must have data which has been **normalised**. This means that the values are displayed in the form of a percentage or a ratio between two values. For example, a student finds the same number of people are living in two different areas, even though one area is much larger than the other. Can you see why it would be wrong to use the same colour for both areas on a choropleth map?

In the example used at the start of this chapter, we could count the number of bus stops found in each Census output area, However, Census output areas are rarely the same size, nor do they have equal populations. In order to make a choropleth map, we should normalise the data by calculating either the number of bus stops per 100 m² or bus stops per 1,000 people.

Figure 3.11 provides another example of this procedure. Raw data recording the number of semi-detached houses in each survey area of a settlement can alternatively be presented as a choropleth map showing semi-detached housing as a percentage of all housing in each area.

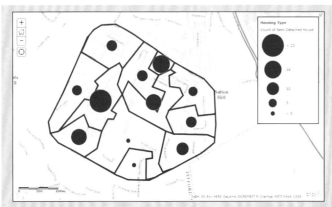

Map with proportional symbols showing count of semi-detached houses in different survey areas. *The count data are presented as proportional symbols. However, the difference between the sizes of the areas means that this map has limited value as an aid for comparing places.*

Choropleth map showing semi-detached houses as a percentage of all houses. *Here, the data have been normalised and a more meaningful analysis can now be carried out.*

Figure 3.11 Two ways of mapping housing data. **Source**: Maps prepared using ArcGIS Online

Mapping points and lines

Figure 3.12 provides a guide to the digital mapping of points, lines and areas. Important points to note are that:

- point and line data can be **categorical** or **ordinal**
- for point and line data it is possible to change the size and colour of the symbols you are using to show two different attributes (for example, you might use the *size* of a symbol to show the mean sediment size found at each point on a beach while varying the *colour* to indicate the modal (most typical) roundness).
- over-use of different symbol shapes, sizes and colours can make your map too confusing, so be on your guard for this!

Figure 3.12 A mapping decision tree. **Source**: ArcGIS Online

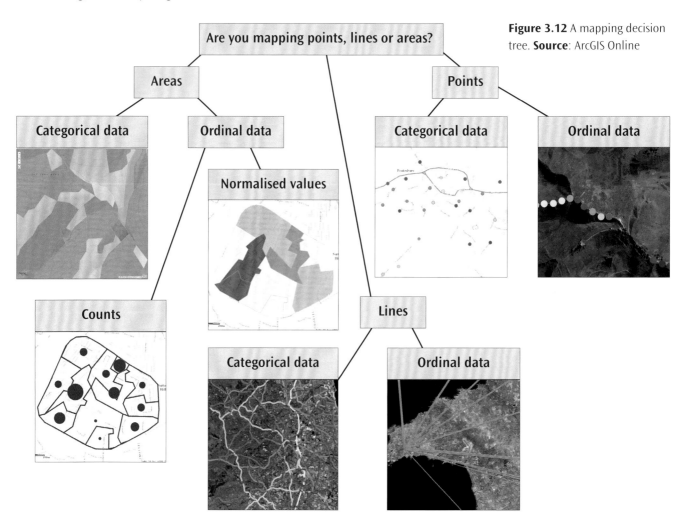

Choosing the right base map

The **base map** on which you choose to present your data can impact on how well your findings are communicated. You may do well to avoid a base map with too much colour which could interfere with the colours of your overlays. Also, the level of detail in the base map can affect the clarity of your data presentation. A map with too much fine detail can overwhelm your own additional data. Think carefully about how much map detail you really need.

Data analysis using GIS

GIS can help you analyse your data. Unlike paper mapping, remember that GIS contains a database which you can continue to access at any point during your data analysis.

- You can use filters to highlight locations that meet particular criteria (such as urban fieldwork locations where a pedestrian count higher than 50 was recorded).
- **Aggregate** and **summarise** tools create an average value for you (e.g. from a number of sample readings within a particular area). For example, environmental quality surveys completed at random points around a settlement could be grouped by postcode and an average value generated and displayed for each postcode.
- **Buffer** functions allow us to create new features based on distance or travel time from existing features. The bus stop survey at the start of the chapter featured a five-minute walk zone (Figure 3.3). This was created using a buffer tool.

Using these and other tools in combination gives you the opportunity to ask very sophisticated and complex questions about your data. You will be able to identify patterns and relationships within your data which otherwise might not become apparent.

Reference

- Darkes, G. and Spence, M. (2008) *Cartography: an introduction*, The British Cartographic Society.

4 Investigating human environments

Objectives

- *Understand ways of carrying out an investigation based on the human geography core topic of changing places.*

- *Know how to establish goals (aims, questions or hypotheses) and select appropriate secondary and primary data sources as part of a valid and achievable methodology.*

The topic of changing places

A place is a portion of geographic space, the identity of which is viewed as being distinctive in some way. Particular places have unique landscapes deriving from underlying physical geography and the way societies have shaped their surface appearance over time.

Every place has its own unique physical site, set of economic functions, population and cultural landscape (Figure 4.1). These elements interact and can change over time. There are also inward and outward flows of people, resources, money and investment to consider (these link a place with other connected places).

The appropriate scale for your independent investigation is a *local* place. The scale of this is likely to be somewhere between a street and a whole settlement. It could be:

- all or a part of a town's Central Business District (CBD)
- one or more urban neighbourhoods or administrative wards (a whole borough would be too large)
- a whole village or small town (as a guideline, it may help to say you can walk around its perimeter in a few hours or less).

It is up to you to decide where the boundaries of your local place are set but remember that secondary data is often most easily obtained at the scale of a council ward.

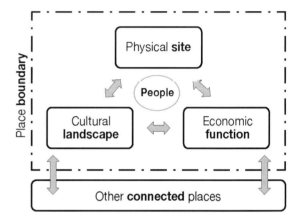

Figure 4.1 Place relationships and connections. **Source**: Simon Oakes

Over to you

Can you create a 'mind map' by applying the elements of Figure 4.1 to a place you know well? Do any good research questions suggest themselves from your mind map?

Inequalities between places

Identifying an aim, question(s) or hypotheses

In Chapter 2, we learned about the importance of establishing clear and achievable aims, questions and/or hypotheses. Figure 4.2 shows how this process of thinking can be applied to the study of inequalities between places.

Specialised concepts (see Chapter 1, page 5) that fit well with this topic include:
- Causality – has a new economic development impacted on inequalities?
- Inequality – how can economic, social and environmental inequality be measured? Have inequalities widened or narrowed over time?
- Globalisation – what is the local impact of the global shift in employment or international migration?
- Mitigation and adaptation – how successful has government intervention been in tackling challenges?

Figure 4.2 Examples of specific questions and hypotheses generated from the investigation aims.

- Resilience – how resilient have rural economies been to agricultural decline? How resilient are CBDs to the growth of online retailing?
- Thresholds – has economic decline crossed the threshold of viability for local village shops?

Aim	Questions	Hypotheses
To investigate whether [ward X] is more deprived than [ward Y] in [city Z]. Example: *To investigate whether Linacre is more deprived than Ravenmeols in Liverpool.*	• What are the income and employment differences between the wards? • What are the education and health differences? • What are the environmental differences, such as building condition and air pollution?	• There is a negative correlation between household income and environmental deprivation. • There is a strong association between unemployment and poor health status.
To investigate whether [recent economic change] has reduced or reinforced economic inequality in [place X]. Example: *To investigate whether the Westfield shopping centre has reduced or reinforced economic inequality in Stratford, London.*	• How is the pattern of social inequality different now compared with 2001? • To what extent is the changing pattern due to economic change? • Are new job opportunities mostly filled by recent incomers rather than longer-term residents?	• The growth of new industry has reduced employment deprivation. • There is less economic inequality there today in comparison with 2001.
To investigate whether [new economic development] has changed the type and distribution of shops in the CBD of [town X]. Example: *To investigate whether online retailing has changed the type and distribution of shops in the CBD of Aylesbury.*	• How have the types and distribution of shops changed since the new development took place? • How far can the changes be explained by the new development? • What other factors could help explain the changing type and distribution of shops?	• There is greater clustering of functions within the CBD than there used to be. • There is now a steeper gradient in shopping quality than there used to be from the centre to the edge of the CBD.
To compare the impact of [recent cultural or demographic change] on [two contrasting villages in the same region]. Example:*To compare the impact of counterurbanisation on Ickford and Shabbington in Oxfordshire.*	• How do functions, land use and buildings differ between the two villages? • How has all of this changed over time? • To what extent is the change explained by recent cultural or demographic changes?	• Land use categories for buildings were very different in 1970 compared with today. • Recent demographic changes have transformed the characteristics of these places.
To investigate how successful [a specific policy] has been in addressing [issue of social deprivation] in [place X]. Example: *To investigate how successful the FareShare initiative has been in providing food to vulnerable people in Nechells, Birmingham.*	• What are the main government or NGO (Non-Government Organisation) interventions in relation to this issue? • Have patterns of social deprivation changed? • To what extent are changing patterns of deprivation linked with government/NGO intervention?	• Government/NGO intervention has reduced social deprivation. • There is less economic deprivation today compared with before the intervention.
To investigate how far [recent migration] has re-shaped the [demographic, socio-economic or cultural characteristics] of [place X]? Example: *To investigate how far EU migration has re-shaped the cultural landscape of Balham, London.*	• What evidence (e.g. size of inflows and outflows) is available to help construct the migration history of place X? • How have the demographic, socio-economic and cultural characteristics of place X changed over time?	• Migration flows have transformed the local society and environment. • There is an association between age of housing and the areas most affected by migration.

What information will help me investigate further?

Let us assume that the focus of your investigation is on inequalities in a particular local place, or the impact of economic or social changes on a particular local place over time. There are three main types of inequality you might study:

- economic inequalities include differentials in the unemployment rate, household incomes and the benefits claimant rate
- social inequalities include people's uneven access to good education and healthcare
- environmental inequalities include variable levels of air pollution and dereliction.

Some of this information is available from Census output data, deprivation indices and other secondary sources (such as local government factsheets and web sites). Other data you will need to collect yourself through primary fieldwork, including questionnaires with local people.

To carry out a temporal study, you might look at economic and social trends over a period of time.

- Important economic trends affecting places in the UK have included the deindustrialisation of inner cities, declining employment in agriculture, the growth of services industries, the expansion of quaternary industry and periods of economic recession and boom.
- Important social trends include increasing longevity (the ageing population), falling fertility and birth rate and accelerating internal migration processes (including gentrification, 'studentification' and counterurbanisation) and rising international migration.

Try to find a concrete local example of a place which has been affected by one of these **macro trends**. The advantage of planning your enquiry in this way is you can demonstrate the wider geographic context your local place study is embedded within.

National (and even global) economic and social trends have all manner of impacts on local places. These can be divided into:

- demographic impacts, e.g. changes in age structure or ethnicity
- socio-economic impacts, e.g. rising or declining economic and social inequalities (including house prices); changing functions, services and job opportunities
- cultural impacts, e.g. changes in a population's language, clothing, food or religion (any of which may be visible in the built environment).

It can sometimes be difficult to find direct evidence of all the historical changes you want to study and you have to rely on proxy data. For example, it is probable that no-one will have actually counted the number of urban-to-rural migrants arriving in a particular village since 1970. However, you could examine 10-yearly census data to see what the total population numbers have been. National-scale data on mortality and fertility trends can help you to estimate how much of your village's changes might be explained by migration rather than changing numbers of births and deaths.

**Top Tip
Adopting a stakeholder focus**
You could study the management of inequalities and economic change by focusing on the actions of national and local government along with other stakeholders. The comparison could be spatial (comparing two places with varying levels of intervention) or temporal (a 'before and after' study of a place which has been managed).

Figure 4.3 Has the opening of Nottingham Science Park in 2010 reduced or reinforced inequalities within the local area? **Source**: Arran Bee (CC BY 2.0)

What information am I going to collect?

Primary data sources

Figure 4.4 Examples of possible primary data foci and collection techniques.

Figure 4.4 provides examples of data collection methods that you could use in your fieldwork. Primary data collection allows us to gather evidence which is not available by any other means.

Data focus	Primary data collection technique	How does this technique help the enquiry?
Economic inequality and patterns, or the impact of economic trends	• Shopping basket survey – comparing the price and range of products.	• The same product can vary in price between shops in different places, raising questions about fairness and equity.
	• Questionnaire survey – investigating how long it takes to reach the shops or bank.	• Provides information on individual people's mobility. The Census output data does not give this level of detail.
	• Field survey – examining local shop types, quality and rate of occupancy.	• Gives information about 'retail health' at a small scale.
Social inequality and patterns, or the impact of social trends	• Bus coverage survey – time taken, frequency, evening and Sunday services.	• Supports the study of unequal access to vital public transport services (see also Chapter 3, page 26).
	• A fieldwork assessment of ease of access for wheelchair users – using photographs and sketches.	• Supports the study of personal mobility and can indicate the social and geographic exclusion of some groups.
	• Questionnaire survey – looking at people's use of new facilities, e.g. sports pitches, cycle paths.	• Can be useful for evaluating success of interventions: are people actually using the new facilities? If not, then why not?
	• Visual survey – documenting graffiti, vandalism and litter levels by varied means.	• Can be used as a proxy measurement for antisocial behaviour (which published crime data may have under-reported).
Environmental inequality and patterns, or the impact of environmental trends	• Environmental quality assessment – using a bipolar scale to map building decay.	• Measures how rundown a place is, supporting Census data (e.g. Census shows homes lacking central heating).
	• Using historical photographs – comparing them with views today.	• Provides vital evidence of historical change using qualitative methods.
	• Field measurements – air pollution can be studied using a smartphone app.	• Allows local level environmental changes and variations to be measured and mapped.

Secondary data sources

Census data and the Index of Multiple Deprivation are essential secondary sources for many investigations undertaken in human geography. Figure 4.5 shows how use can be made of these and other data sources. Figure 4.6 shows mapped 2011 Census data in south-west Birmingham (available at www.datashine.org.uk). This is a digital choropleth map (see Chapter 3, page 31). Areas shaded dark red have a higher percentage of residents educated to degree level. Why is there so much variability and what does it suggest about social and geographic inequalities in the places shown on the map?

Top Tip
Using ONS data
The most reliable secondary source of inequality data is the Index of Multiple Deprivation. A good place to start your enquiry is the ONS Data Explorer.

Type of data	Secondary data source	How do these data help the enquiry?
Economic inequality and patterns, or the impact of economic trends	• 2011 Census: www.datashine.org.uk Historical census data (1971-2001): casweb.ukdataservice.ac.uk	• Both sources provide small area aggregate data on employment, income and benefits (including old age pensions).
	• Land Registry Office: https://www.gov.uk/government/organisations/land-registry	• Provides both historical and up-to-date data on house prices, suggesting areas of affluence and poverty.
	• GOAD maps (paper land use maps archived from the 1960s onwards): http://www.experian.co.uk/goad/education.html	• Valuable source of old mapped data showing shops and services in CBDs; these historical maps can be used to investigate economic change.
	• Index of Multiple Deprivation: https://www.gov.uk/government/statistics/english-indices-of-deprivation-2015	• This provides small area statistics on neighbourhood inequalities.
	• NOMIS official labour market statistics: http://www.nomiswcb.co.uk	• This labour market data may be more up to date than recent Census data.
	• UK broadband availability checker: www.samknows.com	• Useful as a proxy for investigating rural exclusion (poorer areas may be un-served due to lack of demand).
	• Online maps of local services, e.g. maps showing nearest cashpoints: www.link.co.uk/atm-locator	• Useful for investigating unequal access to services that many people in larger settlements take for granted.
	• Rent values for commercial property: www.completelyretail.co.uk	• Useful for estimating the profitability of different retail areas.
Social inequality and patterns, or the impact of social trends	• Crime rates map (searchable by place and month): www.police.uk	• Use this to map street crime, showing variations between different places.
	• Department for Education website: http://www.education.gov.uk	• Useful for investigating school performance data for different places.
	• Sport England's sport participation maps: sae.sportengland.org	• Levels of participation in sport and exercise may be linked with inequality.
	• Datasets from the 2011 Census are mapped at: www.datashine.org.uk	• This covers local population age structure, ethnicity, employment, health status and educational achievement.
Environmental inequality and patterns, or the impact of environmental trends	• Environment Agency mapping: https://www.gov.uk/government/organisations/environment-agency	• Invaluable source of mapped local data on topics including flood risk, erosion and land contamination.
	• Google Street View archives	• Provides important evidence of historical environmental change.
	• Photographs: www.historypin.org	
	• Local archives, e.g. images.manchester.gov.uk	

Figure 4.5
Examples of useful secondary data collection sources.

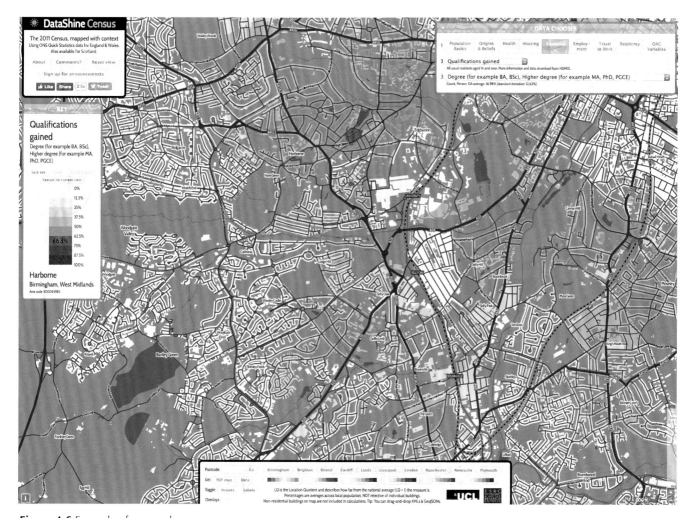

Figure 4.6 Example of mapped 2011 census data using www.datashine.org.uk.
Source: Map data Copyright OpenStreetMap contributors 2015. Census data Crown Copyright

Investigating place meaning, representation and rebranding

'Place meaning and representation' is a topic that most geography students will not have encountered at GCSE-level. It is studied widely at university level where qualitative techniques (such as sensory mapping, semi-structured interviews and discourse analysis) are important research tools.

Place meaning (or identity) is a combination of the real and perceived characteristics of a geographical space. These characteristics can change over time. People's perceptions of a particular place are affected by both their own first-hand experience and by second-hand portrayals in media and art. Sometimes deliberate placemaking efforts aim to change a place's identity. Strategies include regeneration, reimaging and rebranding:

- **Regeneration** includes formal state and private sector attempts to change the fabric of a place by attracting new economic activity and investment to an area or trying to stimulate local enterprise and entrepreneurship.
- **Reimaging** has more to do with the cultural reinvention of place and involves local people and agencies making use of art, photography, film or writing to represent a place in new ways.
- **Rebranding** is a deliberate effort to market a place (e.g. by showing new imagery in adverts and brochures) as desirable for investment and visitors.

You can find an example of data collection for an investigation looking at inequality online.

Details of how to access online resources are on page 3.

Identifying an aim, question(s) or hypotheses

Figure 4.7 shows some clear and achievable aims, questions and/or hypotheses which relate to the study of place meaning, representation and rebranding. Specialised concepts (see Chapter 1, page 13) that fit well with this topic include:

- Globalisation – what is the impact of international migration or investment by global companies (like McDonald's) on people's perceptions of a residential area or town centre?
- Feedback – has the closure of one or more important local businesses led to a spiral of decline? Does the success of a rebranding initiative depend on how much positive feedback it can generate?
- Representations – how is a place represented in art, literature and media?

Figure 4.7 Examples of developing sub-questions and/or hypotheses from your overarching investigation aim or question.

Aim / Research question	Sub-questions	Hypotheses
To investigate how people's identities affect their attitudes to regeneration in [place X]. Example: *To investigate how people's identities affect their attitudes to regeneration in St Mary's, Southampton.*	• What regeneration efforts have been carried out? • How is the regeneration viewed by local residents, business and government? • Why do different people have different priorities for regeneration?	• People are more likely to favour regeneration strategies that bring them a personal benefit. • Newer residents are more likely to have a positive attitude to regeneration than long-term residents.
To investigate whether [short-term festival Y] has had a positive impact on [place Z]. Example: *To investigate whether the Latitude Festival has had a positive impact on the Southwold area.*	• What contribution has the festival made to the surrounding rural economy? • How far away are the trickle-down effects felt? • Are the short-term and long-term impacts of the festival positive overall?	• There is a strong association between distance from the festival site and economic benefit. • Local residents aged 18–35 benefit more from the festival than those aged 65+.
To investigate why the rebranding of [place X] has been a contested process. Example: *To investigate why the rebranding of Arran as a short-break holiday destination has been a contested process.*	• What rebranding efforts have been carried out? • Who was involved? • Why do different stakeholders judge the success of rebranding in different ways?	• Different stakeholders have different perceptions of the success of rebranding. • There is a strong association between stakeholder motivation and positive judgment on the outcomes.
To investigate how far reimaging has changed people's perceptions of [place Y]. Example: *To investigate how far reimaging has changed perceptions of Castle Vale in Birmingham since 1990.*	• What reimaging efforts have been carried out? • How do different people respond to the reimaging? • Is there evidence of a difference in perceptions of place Y before and after reimaging occurred?	• Reimaging has led to a greater proportion of positive newspaper stories. • Reimaging has led to a reduction in local people's fear of crime.
To investigate the representation of [place Z] in [artwork e.g. painting, book or film]. Example: *To investigate the representation of the landscape of the Dorset Heaths in Thomas Hardy's novel Return of the Native.*	• What is the natural and cultural landscape of the place actually like? • What is, and what is not, accurately represented in the artwork? • To what extent does the representation affect the place in real life?	• Artistic representations provide no useful information about what places are actually like. • Artistic representations play an important part in determining how people (e.g. tourists) interact with a real place.

- Identity – how do different people's identities (such as age or ethnicity) affect their perception of a place? How do different people's identities affect their 'lived experience' of a place?
- Sustainability – has the rebranding of a place led to a permanent change in place image which can support the local community and not harm the environment?

What information do you need to investigate place meanings further?

Over to you
Think of a place you might be interested in researching as part of your investigation. What formal and informal data sources could be useful? Could you make use of any artistic or musical data sources?

To start with, you may decide to collect information on the components of place identity to create a **place profile**. This is made using a mix of your own primary fieldwork (such as environmental surveys, photos and sketches) and published secondary information (including Census data).

1. Your first aim could be to produce a valid description of what the place is actually like, i.e. its **objective** characteristics which everybody can agree on.
2. Having done this you could proceed to explore **subjective** characteristics – which people may *not* agree on (one person's 'lively and edgy' neighbourhood may be viewed as 'noisy and threatening' by others, for example). These personal viewpoints are what we mean by place meanings.
3. Some place meanings derive from people's senses. Sight, sound and smell all help us to build up a picture of somewhere in our mind. This can be described as our first-hand lived experience of a place. We form opinions based on other people's representations of places in the media (second-hand sources, such as newspaper articles, television and films).
4. Figure 4.8 suggests some positive and negative perspectives on the place image of different urban neighbourhoods. How could these perspectives have been generated by (i) someone's first-hand experience of a place and (ii) the second-hand representation of that place in different media?

Figure 4.8 Examples of varying perspectives on an urban neighbourhood.

Negative place perspectives	Positive place perspectives
Fear of street crime	Safe
Traffic congestion	Empty roads
Ugly	Picturesque
Poor air quality	Clean air
Lack of green space	Close to nature
Unfriendly	Sense of community
Low social status	High social status

Investigating formal and informal representations of places

An alternative route to collecting data about places is to seek different kinds of **place representation**. These are descriptions of a place and its identity with different types of author and varying claims to be an 'official' place.

- **Formal representations** are produced by a recognised authority such as the local council or a university. Census data is an one essential data source, as we have already learned. You can also use secondary data sources to gather data on the natural features of the landscape (e.g. maps showing a place's geology, soils, rivers, topography) and the cultural features of the landscape (e.g. maps of settlement patterns, field shapes, history). Tourist board brochures are also formal representations of a place. However, they may reveal author bias in the choice of images and themes used to promote a place.
- **Informal (popular) representations** include portrayals in media, paintings, music, fiction, film and television (Figure 4.9). They may represent the views and feelings of a single author and are likely to be biased or subjective in some way or other.

Figure 4.9 Some examples of qualitative data. **Source**: Simon Oakes

You can find examples online of using data collection for an investigation looking at place representations and of data collection for an investigation looking at rural rebranding.

Details of how to access online resources are on page 3.

Investigating placemaking activities

Studies of place reimaging, rebranding and regeneration may consider changes within a place *over time*. Historic data can be compared with present-day data including information collected through fieldwork. Depending on your investigation, you may also need to gather evidence of the attitudes and judgements of different stakeholders. Media representations of place, such as archived newspaper articles, may provide a rich source of information on historic attitudes (but do look for possible writer bias).

What information am I going to collect?

Some perspectives on a place are objective and quantifiable. These can be investigated using published evidence such as Census data. Other perspectives and meanings are subjective. These can be investigated using questionnaires, interviews, mental mapping exercises and observation studies.

Primary data sources

Figure 4.10 provides examples of data collection methods that you could use in your fieldwork.

Secondary data sources

Census data and the Index of Multiple Deprivation are useful secondary sources for place profile investigations (Figure 4.11).

Top Tip
Sampling place representations
Collect a representative, but not *overwhelming*, sample. This might include three paintings by a particular artist, or passages from one or two regional novels. You could use coding (see page 21), image analysis and media analysis to query the words and/or images used to represent the place. If you are investigating the reliability of informal representations, collect first-hand data in the field, such as an environmental quality assessment, in order to make a comparison. Think about using sampling methods in collecting data sources to ensure bias is limited.

Figure 4.10
Examples of possible primary data foci and collection techniques.

Data focus	Primary data collection technique	How does this technique help the enquiry?
Place profile	• Placechecks tool: www.placecheck.info.	A useful first technique for systematically exploring a place and generating possible enquiry questions.
	• Urban townscape survey – annotated photos, field sketches, field survey of townscape elements (building size, materials and condition, open space, street pattern).	Provides objective information on what an urban place is really like. Can be compared with people's perceptions and informal representations of a place.
	• Rural landscape survey – annotated photos, field sketches, landscape survey (building types and styles, land cover, woodland, farms).	Provides objective information on what a rural place is like. Can be compared with people's perceptions and informal representations of a place.
Lived experience of place	• Sensory mapping – noise mapping (soundscape study), aroma (smell) mapping.	Provides information on what people can sense in a place. Secondary data is very unlikely to go into this level of detail.
	• Observation surveys – pedestrian counts and activity surveys.	Records people's actual use of space. Secondary data does not go into this level of detail.
	• Semi-structured interviews (including oral histories).	Particularly useful for capturing historic experiences for which there is limited secondary data.
Place image	• Questionnaires using a bipolar or **Likert** scale.	Generates quantitative data about a sample group's collective attitudes towards a place.
	• Semi-structured interviews.	Provides qualitative information on perceptions of place.
	• Mental mapping (people are asked to sketch a map of a place).	An interesting way of gathering evidence of how people view the size, contents and boundaries of a place.
	• Social media analysis (including coding of text and images).	A relatively new way of studying how people write about where they visit/live.
Represent-ations of place	• Discourse analysis of text, images and film (e.g. image analysis, coding of creative writing).	Shows how a place is portrayed in the media, and whether certain features are over-represented or under-represented.
Placemaking (including reimaging, rebranding and regeneration)	• Comparing historical photographs with views today.	Provides evidence of historical change in a place profile.
	• Field survey of shop type, quality and occupancy.	Shows retail health at a small scale; can be compared with historic data.
	• Discourse analysis of marketing material (e.g. brochures, websites).	Shows how a place is marketed to residents and outsiders; can also identify target audience (niche groups).
	• Semi-structured interviews with stakeholders (e.g. local residents, small businesses, tourist officers).	Creates a picture of conflicts occurring over place representations.

43

Data focus	Secondary data sources and collection techniques	How does this technique help the enquiry?
Place profile and formal representations of place	• 2011 Census: www.datashine.org.uk • Historical census data (1971–2001): casweb.ukdataservice.ac.uk	Provides small area statistics for employment, income and benefits, including old age pensions.
	• Geo-demographic data such as ACORN: acorn.caci.co.uk	Provides objective data on socio-economic characteristics of places.
	Natural landscape: • British Geological Survey open data: www.bgs.ac.uk/opengeoscience. • UK Soil Observatory: www.ukso.org/maps.html	Provides a formal representation of what the physical setting of a place is like (which can be compared with artistic portrayals).
	Cultural landscape (rural): • Settlement patterns and field shapes can be observed on a 1:25000 OS map. • Genuki: a gateway to access historic information for most small settlements in England www.genuki.org.uk. • National Character Areas by Natural England (https://www.gov.uk/government/publications/national-character-area-profiles-data-for-local-decision-making).	Provides a formal (authoritative) representation of what the cultural landscape of a rural place is like (such as settlement patterns, field shapes, building materials and important history). For example: www.devon.gov.uk/landscapecharacter
	Cultural landscape (urban): • Historic Area Assessments and Historic Town Characterisation (see www.historicengland.co.uk or websites of local authorities).	Provides a formal representation of what the cultural landscape of an urban place is like (such as street patterns, building age, building materials, building styles).
	Historical photographs: • www.historypin.org. • Google Street View archives. • www.britainfromabove.org.	Provides evidence of historical change over time.
Placemaking (including reimaging, rebranding and regeneration)	Economic indicators: • House prices (Land Registry) • Rent values for commercial property (www.completelyretail.co.uk) • Employment (nomisweb.co.uk).	Can compare data before and after new placemaking (e.g. rebranding) has occurred.
	Social indicators: • Crime rates (www.police.uk). • Health status (Census data such as www.datashine.org.uk). • School results (search on www.gov.uk).	Can compare data before and after new placemaking (e.g. regeneration) has occurred.
	• Environmental indicators, such as traffic congestion, published visitor surveys, coastal Blue Flag surveys.	Can compare data before and after placemaking has occurred.
	• Coding of texts, such as historic and present-day newspapers and letters.	Can reveal changing representations, perceptions, and possible conflicts.

Figure 4.11
Examples of possible secondary data foci, sources and collection techniques.

Further reading

- 'What makes a great place?' by the project for Public Spaces (https://www.pps.org) is a useful model which showcases rigour in fieldwork design.

- Analysis of media images can be explored at: www.mediaknowall.com (popular website for teachers and students of A level media studies, including detailed guidance on carrying out image analysis).

- Royal Town Planning Institute: guidance on education and careers in 'making of place', with links to materials developed with the RGS-IBG: www.rtpi.org.uk

- Useful sources of secondary data on inequality include:
  - Index of Multiple Deprivation at https://www.gov.uk/government/statistics/english-indices-of-deprivation-2015
  - Office of National Statistics Data Explorer page: https://www.ons.gov.uk/help/localstatistics

References

- Detailed background information prepared by the Office for National Statistics, including planning for the 2021 census: www.ons.gov.uk/census

- Phillips, R. and Johns, J. (2012) *Fieldwork for Human Geography.* Sage Publications: London.

- Hay, I. (ed) (2016) *Qualitative Research Methods in Human Geography.* OUP A detailed undergraduate guide to qualitative data collection (including questionnaires, interviews, focus groups and participant observation) and data analysis (including concept mapping and coding).

5 Investigating physical environments

Objectives

- *Understand how to carry out an investigation based on the physical geography core topics of*

    (i) water and carbon cycles and

    (ii) landscape systems.

- *Understand the initial stages of the enquiry process: these include establishing goals (aims, questions or hypotheses) and the selection of appropriate secondary and primary data sources as part of a valid and achievable methodology.*

Water and carbon cycles

Study of the water and carbon cycles is a core element of A level geography (Figure 5.1).

An enquiry into the water cycle might allow you to deepen your understanding of geographical ideas and theories about evaporation, precipitation, run-off generation, catchment hydrology, water extraction and groundwater, land use change or even cryospheric processes. Studies of rivers and drainage basins have long been a mainstay of GCSE and A level geography: there are many published resources and textbooks that can assist you.

In contrast, the carbon cycle has received less attention until recently: working within this relatively novel topic area could be a good way to demonstrate your independence. This might involve carrying out a geographical field investigation which relates in some way to the processes of photosynthesis, decomposition, fossil fuel combustion, land use change, weathering, sediments or movements and sequestration of dissolved carbon. Alternatively, an enquiry could be focused around carbon sinks or stores, including forest or peat moorland management strategies.

Figure 5.1 The water cycle and the carbon cycle. **Source**: Adapted from United States Geological Survey graphic.

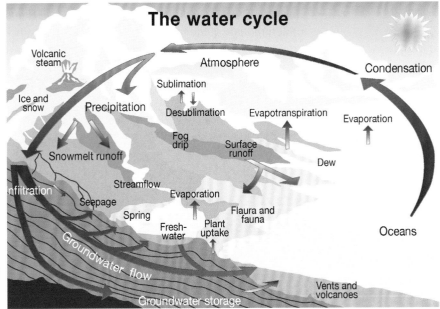

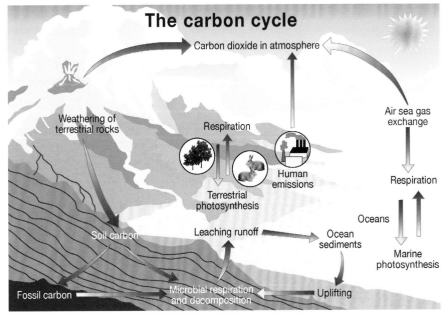

Investigating the water cycle

"This flood was not only foretold – it was publicly subsidised"

Figure 5.2 How George Monbiot began his report on flooding in Yorkshire on 29 December 2015. **Source:** the *Guardian*. Photo: Asadour Guzelian

Identifying an aim, question(s) or hypothesis

You may want to conduct an enquiry which extends your classroom learning of the water cycle and its components as a system. Alternatively, news reports and recent research articles could provide a starting point for your independent investigation. Most of the UK's major news websites organise articles by topic area. Try searching for 'flooding' or 'climate change' on the BBC or Guardian websites. The 2015 winter floods in northern England received huge media coverage; writers such as George Monbiot have explored the interconnections between upland land management, urbanisation, rivers and flooding. This kind of writing inspires a range of geographic questions about the causes and impacts of these floods at the local level and how we can best manage river catchments in the future.

Specialised concepts (see Chapter 1, page 13) that fit well with this topic include:
- Causality – has land use management caused changes in water flows?
- Systems and equilibrium – what is the pattern of water inputs and outputs in a small drainage basin?
- Interdependence – how are the soil, vegetation and water flows interrelated?
- Risk and resilience – how resilient are flood protection measures against extreme weather risks associated with climate change?
- Mitigation and adaptation – what actions can be taken to ameliorate overland flow?
- Sustainability – how can rivers be managed or restored in sustainable ways?
- Thresholds – what is the threshold rainfall event for flooding in a certain river catchment?

Once you have identified a broad topic area of interest, it is time to establish clear and achievable aims, questions and/or hypotheses (Figure 5.4).

Figure 5.3 A small-scale stream catchment: what geographic questions are suggested by this image? **Source**: Daniel House

How long does it take for a rainfall event to peak as discharge in the stream?

How much of the water falling on this catchment ends up in the river?

How do different land uses impact the hydrology of a river catchment?

How does this catchment impact on communities and people downstream?

Aim	Questions	Hypotheses
To investigate how [river x] has been affected by management. Example: *To investigate how Loughton Brook has been affected by land management.*	• How has the river been managed? • Has the river changed and how? • Are these changes a result of management?	• River management has increased river discharge. • River management has changed the storm hydrograph of the river.
To investigate how land use affects catchment response to rainfall in [river valley x]. Example: *To investigate how land use affects catchment response to rainfall in North Glen Sannox.*	• How does land use affect infiltration and run-off? • How do different soil types respond to rainfall events?	• Catchments with impermeable geology have flashy river hydrographs. • Woodland catchments have a different river response compared with open fields.
To investigate how the behaviour of [river x] impacts on local communities. Example: *To investigate how the behaviour of the River Wandle impacts on local communities.*	• What are the different river responses to rainfall in this catchment? • Who lives downstream and what impacts have they seen in the past?	• This catchment will have an impact on people downstream. • People's lives are adversely affected by the behaviour of this river.

What information am I going to collect?

Figure 5.4 Examples of how more specific questions and hypotheses are generated from the main aim of the investigation.

Choosing a context at an appropriate scale is essential. A study of a small hill stream or river catchment will be most manageable. Also aim to focus on processes occurring over hours and days, such as infiltration or run-off, rather than annual or decadal water cycle dynamics (although you may find secondary data relating to water flows over longer time frames).

You can identify the closest gauging station to your proposed field site(s) through the National River Flow Archive (NRA) website. The GOV.UK website provides information about UK River Basin Management Plans which may provide you with a huge amount of data relating to your case study stream or river.

Figure 5.5 shows small-scale catchment data. It is freely available from the Centre for Ecology and Hydrology Flood Estimation Handbook service at https://fehweb.ceh.ac.uk.

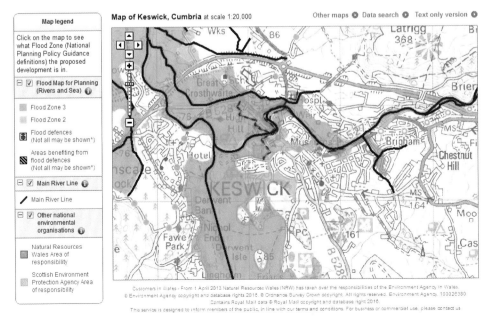

Figure 5.5 Small-scale catchment example of Glenderaterra Beck, which is a tributary of the Greta and Derwent rivers in Cumbria. It is part of the system that caused extensive flooding in Keswick in the 2015 winter floods and is a good example of a suitable sized catchment at approximately 11km². **Source**: Flood Estimation Handbook Web Service, Centre for Ecology and Hydrology.

Primary data sources

Having selected a case study context, what primary data can you collect? Figure 5.6 provides examples of data collection methods that you could use to investigate water flows. In addition, you could make use of qualitative data, including photographs, field sketches or interviews with residents or managers. The main thing is to adopt methods which suit your investigation and will help get answers to the questions you want to ask.

Figure 5.6 Primary data collection techniques for an enquiry focused on water flows.

Rainfall data	Collecting data from rain gauges (free of vegetation cover) on hourly or daily basis.
Interception data	Making use of data from rain gauges situated below vegetation cover, e.g. coniferous woodland or deciduous woodland.
Stem flow data	Estimating the amount or rate of flow of water down tree branches. (Can you think of a way of doing this?)
Infiltration data	Measuring the rate at which water infiltrates into different soils, land surfaces and/or slope angles (using a cylinder and stop watch).
Run-off data	Measuring the rate at which water of a certain depth moves over different land surfaces, e.g. vegetated and non-vegetated slopes.
River channel discharge data	Measuring the channel size and velocity of water in a channel will enable you to calculate the amount of water per second (i.e. the discharge measured in **cumecs**). This could also be calculated for the bank full capacity of a channel (the maximum discharge prior to flooding). There are various methods which can be used including use of a current meter. For example, see: http://water.usgs.gov/edu/streamflow2.html
Evaporation and transpiration data	There are various ways of estimating the water loss from evaporation and transpiration. For example, see: http://theconstructor.org/water-resources/evaporation-and-its-measurement/4575

You can find an example online of data collection for an investigation looking at infiltration and land use.

Details of how to access online resources are on page 3.

Secondary data sources

The following are good sources for background information and useable secondary data:

- USGS, general introduction to hydrology: http://water.usgs.gov/wsc/glossary.html
- National River Flow Archive (data search): http://nrfa.ceh.ac.uk/data/search
- GOV.UK river basin management plans (2015): https://www.gov.uk/government/collections/river-basin-management-plans-2015
- Environment Agency flood maps: https://flood-map-for-planning.service.gov.uk
- Catchment Change Management Hub: http://ccmhub.net/
- Catchment data explorer (Environment Agency): http://environment.data.gov.uk/catchment-planning/
- Rainfall run-off analysis: http://www.fao.org/docrep/u3160e/u3160e05.htm
- UK Met Office (an excellent source of climate and rainfall information): http://www.metoffice.gov.uk/public/weather/climate/gcty8njjs
- The NRFA (gives daily and historic flow data from gauging stations): https://nrfa.ceh.ac.uk
- The CEH website (gives monthly hydrological summaries for the UK which might help explain the antecedent conditions of field sites): http://nrfa.ceh.ac.uk/monthly-hydrological-summary-uk

Secondary data sources will support your water cycle enquiry in many ways. For instance, the Met Office has data detailing the monthly and annual average rainfall data in Keswick, northern England and the UK as a whole. Keswick receives higher-than-average rainfall across the year and especially in the months of October through to January. This information suggests that October is a good month to collect primary data there (if you are interested in studying a catchment's response to rainfall).

Top Tip
Using technical documents
Some technical documents can be very detailed so it is important to use careful judgement when picking out key facts and figures. Don't use large amounts of technical information as 'padding' for your investigation.

Investigating the carbon cycle

Identifying an aim, question(s) or hypothesis

Alongside the water cycle, you will also be studying the carbon cycle as part of A level geography. Fossil fuel use (for energy, transportation and plastics) has altered the balance of stores in the global carbon system, including atmospheric carbon (leading to climate change). It doesn't take long to find plenty of secondary data about carbon online. Intergovernmental Panel on Climate Change (IPCC) reports are a highly reputable source of information, for instance.

Understanding how the carbon cycle functions as a physical system could be integral to your independent investigation. Thinking about how natural processes and **anthropogenic** activity influence carbon stores and/or **fluxes** may help you identify an appropriate and manageable study scale and focus. For example, you could enquire about the cycling associated with the carbon budget of a small field or river catchment.

Figure 5.7 shows some information sources on the carbon cycle which you may already have studied in class. They could also be a good starting for your enquiry's literature review and for identifying a focus for your enquiry.

Top Tip
Linking a global system with a local study
Make sure you set out your enquiry aim(s) clearly and contextualise what you are doing. You will be carrying out a local-scale investigation in order to apply and extend your knowledge and understanding of a much larger-scale global system.

Focus	Source	Link
The global carbon cycle	University of New Hampshire	http://globecarboncycle.unh.edu/CarbonCycleBackground.pdf
The carbon story	British Geological Survey	http://www.bgs.ac.uk
Carbon storage and sequestration	Natural England	http://publications.naturalengland.org.uk/file/94024
Carbon storage and ecological habitats	Natural England	http://publications.naturalengland.org.uk/publication/1412347
Carbon and climate change	Natural England	http://publications.naturalengland.org.uk/category/40003
Soil fieldwork ideas	Soil Carbon Coalition	http://soilcarboncoalition.org/challenge

Figure 5.7 Information sources for carbon cycle studies.

Once you have identified a broad topic are of interest, it is time to establish clear and achievable aims, questions and/or hypotheses (Figure 5.8). Specialised concepts (see Chapter 1, page 13) that fit well with this topic include:
- Causality – has land use management caused changes in carbon stores and flows?
- Systems and equilibrium – what is the pattern of carbon inputs and outputs in a small area?
- Globalisation – how are people's carbon footprints affected by globalisation?
- Mitigation and adaptation – what actions can be taken in relation to anthropogenic carbon emissions?
- Sustainability – how can carbon stores (peat, soils, ecosystems) be managed sustainably?
- Risk and resilience – what threats to carbon stores are associated with land use change or soil erosion?

Inter-disciplinary links with chemistry and biology (if you are studying either subject) might also assist your geographical investigation into carbon cycle operations or issues.

Aim	Questions	Hypotheses
To investigate how much carbon is stored /cycled in [carbon store x]. Example: *To investigate how much carbon is stored in Formby Woods.*	• How much carbon enters and leaves the forest? • How much carbon is stored in peat moorland?	• Peat moorland is a significant store of organic matter containing carbon. • Carbon losses from peat moorland are increasing because of land use changes.
To investigate carbon sequestration in [ecosystem X]. Example: *To investigate carbon sequestration in Epping Forest's oak trees.*	• How much carbon does an oak tree sequester monthly or annually in biomass? • How far would increasing the area of UK woodlands help with climate change mitigation?	• Trees play an important role in the sequestration of carbon. • Afforestation is an effective means of tackling climate change.
To investigate the impact of soil erosion on carbon cycling in [location X]. Example: *To investigate the impact of soil erosion on carbon cycling in the Peak District.*	• How much carbon is sequestered in soils? • How much carbon is lost through soil erosion?	• Soil erosion creates a net decrease in carbon storage. • Soil erosion is transferring organic carbon to other stores, e.g. sedimentary rocks.

Figure 5.8 Examples of how more specific questions and hypotheses are generated from the main aim of the investigation.

What information am I going to collect?

The decision to focus on a specific part of the carbon cycle will influence your choice of fieldwork location (or vice versa). Terrestrial carbon and its flux with the atmosphere (sometimes called 'fast carbon') is one of the more obvious sub-systems to investigate. Biomass and carbon sequestration within woodlands (Figure 5.9), peat bogs or agricultural soil are study foci with well-established theories and data which you can research in order to support your A level investigation. Also, they offer the prospect of simple, small-scale (and thus manageable) fieldwork locations.

Figure 5.9 The woodland carbon cycle: what fieldwork would enable you to calculate how much carbon is in a tree? **Source**: Adapted from Fig 1, Open Journal of Ecology Vol.2 No.3 (2012)

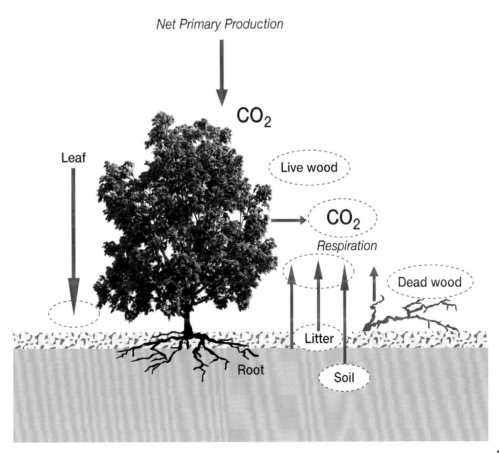

Primary data sources

Figure 5.10 shows possible primary data sources for an investigation of the carbon cycle. This could involve quantitative measurement of a store or flux of carbon (you can investigate the role of carbon dioxide in the growth or death of different plant or animal groups). Alternatively, an investigation could focus on carbon dioxide released from heather burning in uplands. These are plenty of opportunities to study movements of carbon dioxide in solution (which allows you to establish synoptic links with the water cycle topic).

Estimating carbon storage in trees and woodlands	The volume of a tree can be calculated using its diameter at breast height (dbh) and total height. Once the volume is known, dry tonnes of biomass can be calculated for the tree species. Carbon weight is calculated as being approximately 50 per cent of its dry biomass. Find out more in the Carbon Assessment Protocol at https://forestry.gov.uk
Estimating carbon storage in peat	The volume of carbon stored in an area of peat moorland or bog can be estimated by measuring its depth and area. The carbon content can then be calculated along with its age (secondary data are needed to establish this) and carbon sequestration rates. Find out more at: http://www.iucn-uk-peatlandprogramme.org/
Estimating carbon storage in in soil	'Loss on ignition' experiments can give accurate results showing how much organic carbon is stored in soil. Find out more at: https://www.sfu.ca/soils/lab_documents/Estimation_Of_Organic_Matter_By_LOI.pdf
Measuring plant respiration and photosynthesis	Carbon dioxide measuring probes can be used in conjunction with a plant and plastic bag to monitor and record changes in carbon dioxide and other parameters, for example temperature. http://www.saps.org.uk/secondary/teaching-resources/157-measuring-the-rate-of-photosynthesis

Figure 5.10 Potential primary data sources for a carbon investigation.

Top Tip
Choosing the right time of year
Opportunities to study biomass accumulation and sequestration may be dependent on seasonality and so require careful planning. Investigations into photosynthesis or respiration will be largely limited to summer months. If you are combining carbon and water studies – perhaps by examining soil erosion, suspended sediments or the transport of carbon within river systems – you may want to work with rainfall events during autumn months.

Secondary data sources

Information and secondary data on carbon flows, stores and footprints can be obtained from various professional organisations and sources (although the data are often large-scale, e.g. at the national level). The Forestry Commission is a good source for woodland data (Figure 5.11). So too is the RSPB, which published *Peatbogs and Carbon* in 2010. This technical report provides examples of how carbon storage calculations are arrived at.

Table 1   Carbon stored by British-grown trees and their timber products

Site type	Tree species	Yield class (m³/hectare/annum)	Equivalent carbon yield (tonnes/hectare/annum)	Normal rotation (years)	Period to maximum carbon fixation (years)	Average amount of carbon in a fixed form at time of maximum (tonnes/hectare)
Upland	Sitka spruce	12	1.7	55	110	78
	Scots pine	8	1.4	70	140	74
	Birch	4	1.0	45	90	61
Lowland	Scots pine	10	1.7	65	130	91
	Corsican pine	16	2.7	50	100	135
	Oak	6	1.5	150	300	118

Figure 5.11 Estimates of carbon storage in British trees.
Source: Forestry Commission , Research Information Note 160 'The storage of carbon in trees and timber'.

You can find an example online of data collection for an investigation looking at carbon sequestration.

Details of how to access online resources are on page 3.

Landscape systems

Study of landscape systems is the other core element of physical geography at A level. An enquiry into either coastal or glacial environments can deepen your understanding of the processes of erosion, transport and deposition, as well as the time-scales they operate over. Another approach might be to investigate patterns and distributions within particular landscapes, or to assess how distinctive these and other features are. Alternatively, management issues and challenges could become your focus.

Figure 5.12 shows elements of a coastal system while Figure 5.13 shows a glacial system. As you can see, in each case there are many different processes and landscape elements to investigate, along with the system inputs, outputs and flows of energy and material which give rise to these and other features. Both coastal and glacial landscapes therefore offer ample opportunity for you to develop an individual investigation.

Figure 5.12 Elements of a coastal landscape.
Source: Simon Oakes

Figure 5.13 Elements of a glacial landscape.
Source: Richard Waller

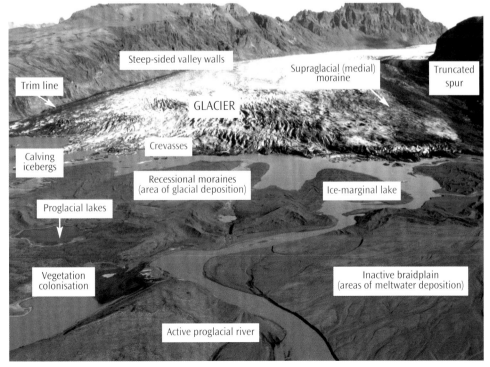

Investigating coastal landscapes

Identifying an aim, question(s) or hypothesis

You may want to conduct an enquiry which extends your classroom learning of coastal landscapes and processes. Your studies will have included some or all of the following: high energy coasts and their geomorphological processes (rocky and sandy coastlines); low energy coasts and their geomorphological processes (e.g. estuarine coastlines); the way that winds, waves and currents interact to create flows and stores of sediments in the coastal zone; retreating coastlines and how they are managed; coastal habitats, e.g. salt marsh and sand dunes); climate change impacts along the coast, human activity and coastal management.

If you are especially interested in one of these topics, then that is a good reason to focus your enquiry on it. Equally, your focus will be influenced by which particular coastline you intend to study and the components that make up its coastal zone (e.g. its geology, fetch, sediment dynamics, tidal regime, land uses and management approaches). In particular, you will need to identify:
- whether it is a high or low energy coast
- if processes such as longshore drift or cliff erosion or deposition have a large influence there
- if it is heavily managed and/or populated
- whether this coast is thought of mainly as a tourist resource, a natural flood defence, an ecological habitat, or a combination of these.

A background check of your intended location(s) can be carried out using local visitor websites and shoreline management plans (SMP) and maps. Using your knowledge of coastal theories and ideas, think of some geographical questions you might try to answer as part of your investigation. For instance, Figure 5.14 shows an Ordnance Survey map extract and photograph of Minehead on the West Somerset Coast:
- The main coastal features here are characteristic of a low energy estuarine coastline (the Bristol Channel).
- Sand and shingle beaches front the coastline, with a sediment drift from west to east.
- There is map evidence of low-lying marsh areas in the east near the Holiday Village.
- The town has coastal defences in the form of breakwaters and a sea wall constructed in 2000 (an online search reveals that spring tides have contributed historically to flooding of the town and the low lying land to the east). Large waves are propagated by westerly Atlantic storms.

Based on this evidence, what enquiry questions can you think of?

Figure 5.14 Ordnance Survey map of Minehead (1:50 000) and a photograph of its coastal defenses. **Source:** map: Ordnance Survey © Crown Copyright; Photo: Daniel House

Specialised concepts that fit well with the study of coastal landscapes and systems include:

- Causality – how do winds and waves interact to shape this environment?
- Systems and equilibrium – what is the pattern of sediment input and output movements?
- Mitigation and adaptation – what actions can be taken in relation to the flooding and erosion?
- Sustainability – how can this coastal environment and settlement be managed sustainably?
- Risk and resilience – what actions are being taken in relation to climate change projections?

Figure 5.15 Examples of how more specific questions and hypotheses are generated from the main aim of the investigation.

Once you have identified a broad topic are of interest, it is time to establish clear and achievable aims, questions and/or hypotheses (Figure 5.15).

Aim	Questions	Hypotheses
To investigate how [coast X] is managed and whether the benefits outweigh the costs. Example: *To investigate the costs and benefits of coastal management in Prestatyn.*	• What is the current and/or projected management plan for this coastline? • What are the costs and benefits and how might they change in the future?	• This coastline should be abandoned to managed retreat. • The future benefits of coastal management will outweigh the projected costs.
To investigate sediment stores and flows along [coast X]. Example: *To investigate sediment stores and flows along Lamlash beach.*	• What are the most important factors affecting coastal processes here? • How are inputs, outputs and flows of sediment interrelated in this location? • Do anthropogenic influences affect the system?	• Longshore drift moves sediment eastwards. • Erosion and transportation of sediment have led to the sorting of beach material. • Groynes have interrupted natural processes of sediment cycling here.
To investigate the concept of Integrated Coastal Zone Management in [location X]. Example: To *investigate Integrated Coastal Zone Management in Loch Etive.*	• What is the environmental, economic, social, cultural and recreational value of this coastline? • How resilient is the coastline to future changes?	• Coastal management offers a sustainable future to this coast and its people. • Some stakeholders benefit more than others from coastal management.

What information am I going to collect?

Figure 5.12 showed an example of a coastal landscape. Once you have narrowed your enquiry focus – while also possibly making use of specialised concepts, such as systems or risk – you will need to decide which kinds of primary and secondary data will best support your investigation.

Primary data sources

Suggested quantitative and qualitative approaches to primary data collection are shown in Figure 5.16. More detailed descriptions of these measurement techniques and observational skills are widely available in text books and online.

Secondary data sources

The following are all useful sources of secondary technical information and data to support coastal fieldwork data collection. They will also help you to read about and understand your case study context and the way its coastal system operates.

- Shoreline management plans:
  https://www.gov.uk/government/publications/shoreline-management-plans-smps
- Environment Agency flooding and coastal change information (flood and erosion

Beach profiles	A systematic or stratified sampling method can be used (see Chapter 2) to measure the gradient, size and shape of a beach using **clinometers** or levelling equipment.
Cliff profiles	Clinometers and a tape measure can be used to record the main contours and height of cliffs. Field observations and photographs of structure, bedding planes, mass movement and slope processes can all be taken.
Sediment petrology	There are many ways sediment can be investigated, including:sediment size (recording the A, B and C axis lengths), shape classification (using classes such as blades, rods, discs and spheres), the **Cailleux Index** of roundness. Sedimentary petrology is also concerned with environments of deposition including interpretation of transportation and deposition processes.
Wave type	Waves can be studied in relation to their frequency (how many waves per minute). Field observations and photographs can be taken of plunging or spilling waves.
Sea defence analysis	A bipolar evaluation can be carried out of different sea defences (awarding scores in order to compare different aspects of the defences). Hudson's equation is used to assesses the ability of riprap to withstand wave action. Human perceptions of the effectiveness and aesthetics of defences can be measured using questionnaires.
Coastal process mapping	Observations can be made of longshore drift sediment movements using **tracers** and field observations. Evidence of processes can be added later to base maps.
Coastal defence mapping	Observations can be made of coastal defences. Evidence of their condition can be quantified and indexed (based on field observations).
Land use mapping	Mapping of land uses can be carried out in areas most clearly at risk from flooding or erosion.

maps): https://www.gov.uk/topic/environmental-management/flooding-coastal-change
- Geology maps:
  http://www.bgs.ac.uk/discoveringGeology/geologyOfBritain/viewer.html
- The UK tide gauge network (showing sea level heights):
  https://www.bodc.ac.uk/data/online_delivery/ntslf/
- Elevation Finder (helping you find the height of land in your case study area):
  https://www.freemaptools.com/elevation-finder.htm
- Intergovernmental Panel on Climate Change (global climate and sea level projections): http://www.ipcc.ch

Figure 5.16 Primary data collection techniques suited to a coastal landscape enquiry.

Figure 5.17 Minehead management policies to 2030 (investigating these choices could form the basis for an enquiry).
Source: Environment Agency

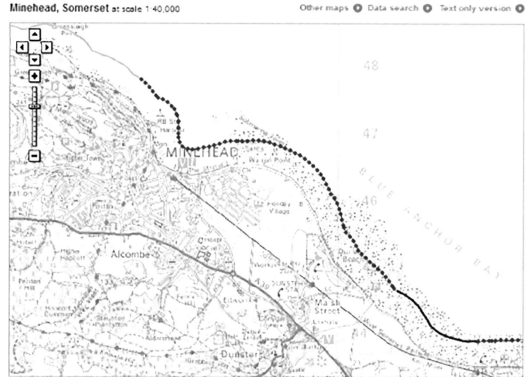

The Environment Agency (EA) holds extensive data sets which can be invaluable when carrying out coastal research. For instance, Figure 5.17 is an annotated map produced by the Environment Agency showing the agreed types of management policy for Minehead between now and 2030. In most of this area the intention is to hold the existing defence line. Why might that decision have been taken?

Coastal observatory groups are another useful source of secondary data. For example, the Plymouth Coastal Observatory website provides information about the southwest of the UK, such as Figure 5.18 which shows sediment distribution around Minehead. This could be used in conjunction with primary data to support beach fieldwork. Also, some universities (such as Southampton) are deeply involved with shoreline management and may have data they can share.

Figure 5.18 The distribution of sediment types in Minehead Bay. **Source**: Channel Coast Observatory

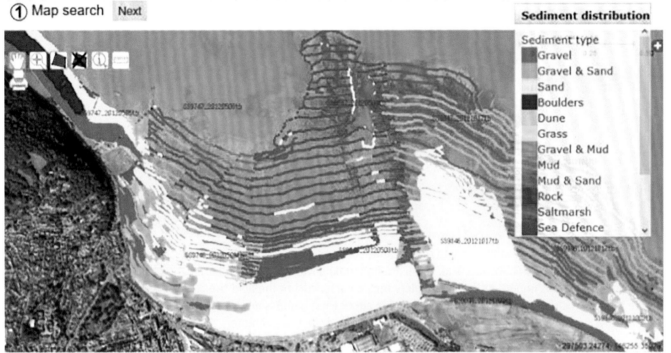

① Map search   Next

Sediment distribution

Sediment type
Gravel
Gravel & Sand
Sand
Boulders
Dune
Grass
Gravel & Mud
Mud
Mud & Sand
Rock
Saltmarsh
Sea Defence

You can find an example online of data collection for an investigation looking at sediment transport.

Details of how to access online resources are on page 3.

Investigating glacial landscapes
Identifying an aim, question(s) or hypothesis

Glacial landscapes are characterised by a broad range of processes, landforms and sediments and they include some of the most diverse and spectacular landscapes on Earth. These environments can be investigated using a range of desk-based, field-based and laboratory-based techniques in order to collect qualitative and quantitative data suitable for an independent research project. Landscapes within large parts of the U.K., Europe and North America have been affected by past glaciation and contain a long-lasting legacy of relict (historical) glacial landforms and sediments. If you have the opportunity to undertake your project in a currently glaciated environment such as Iceland or the Alps, then there is an even broader range of opportunities available, including the possibility of investigating active glacial processes.

Possible topics, issues and features for your investigation could include:
* glacier mass balance and the relationship between glaciers and climate
* the processes of erosion, transport and deposition operating at different spatial and temporal scales
* the transfer of debris through the glacial system
* the nature and origin of a broad range of glacial landforms
* the combination of different landforms to produce distinctive landscapes
* the influence of past and present climate change or human activity.

The type of project that you will be able to complete will depend inevitably upon the possible field locations you have access to. If you are undertaking your research as part of a class field trip, it is important that you explore the characteristics of the field site before the trip to identify its key characteristics and to check what is and is not feasible. Specific ways in which you can do this include viewing the field site using remotely-sensed imagery (Figure 5.19) or searching for secondary data on the glacial features in your study area.

Once you have considered your field site, you can develop your project ideas further. At this stage, it is important that you undertake a more thorough review of the relevant research literature. You can make use of search engines like Google Scholar that will identify articles in academic research journals and show you what research questions are being addressed by professional glaciologists currently. Engaging with this glacial literature will enable you to place your own project within its broader geographical context, which is an essential component of independent research at A level.

Specialised concepts that fit well with the study of coastal landscapes and systems include:
- Causality – how have past ice movements and post–glacial processes shaped this landscape?
- Systems – what evidence is there for historical patterns of sediment flows?
- Mitigation and adaptation – what actions are taken in relation to the safety risks which are present in currently glaciated environments?
- Sustainability – how can cold environments be managed sustainably?
- Risk and resilience – what actions are being taken in relation to climate change projections for currently glaciated regions, including ski resorts?

Once you have identified a broad topic are of interest, it is time to establish clear and achievable aims, questions and/or hypotheses (Figure 5.20).

Figure 5.19 Three-dimensional oblique view of the Snowdon Horseshoe from Google Earth that can be used to visualise the glacial landforms present at the site. **Source**: Google Earth

Top Tip
Working abroad
Visiting an exotic location can help make your NEA unusual and interesting. However, it also makes it difficult to re-visit your fieldwork site should you need to carry out any follow-up work. You must plan overseas fieldwork very carefully.

Aim	Questions	Hypotheses
To investigate the characteristics of the glacier that occupied [study site] during the most recent phase of glaciation. Example: *To investigate the characteristics of the glacier that occupied Cwm Idwal during the most recent phase of glaciation.*	• What relict glacial landforms can be identified and what do they reveal about the characteristics of the glacier? • What was the maximum extent of the glacier?	• The glacier accomplished processes of both erosion and deposition.The glacier was warm-based with active basal sliding.The glacier transported a mixture of subglacial and supraglacial sediment.
To investigate the influence of aspect on the morphometry of cirques in [study area.] Example: *To investigate the influence of aspect on the morphometry of cirques in Snowdonia.*	• How does cirque morphometry (e.g. width, length, height of back wall etc.) vary with aspect? • Has geology and local structure exerted an influence on cirque morphometry?	• Cirques on slopes orientated towards the NE are larger and more deeply incised (i.e. they have a higher backwall). • Cirques oriented parallel to local faults are larger and more deeply incised.
To investigate the past glacial environments at [study site] through an analysis of glacial sediments. Example: *To reconstruct the past glacial environments at Glanllynnau, North Wales through an analysis of the glacial sediments exposed in the coastal cliffs.*	• What different types of sediment are evident in the exposed sequence? • How many phases of glaciation can be identified through tills analysis? • What do the tills indicate about ice flow directions and sediment pathways?	• The site was influenced my multiple phases of glaciation. • The ice flow affecting the area was from the [add direction]. • The tills present were formed by subglacial deposition.
*To investigate temporal variations in the recession of [study site]. Example: *To investigate variations in the recession of Skaftafellsjökull, Iceland.*	• How many moraine limits can be identified? • How do the rates of glacier recession vary over time?	• The rates of glacier recession vary through time. • The rate of glacier recession increased in the middle part of the 20th Century.

Figure 5.20 Examples of how specific questions and hypotheses can be developed from the main aim of the investigation. *The asterisk highlights a project that could be undertaken in a modern-day glacial environment.

What information am I going to collect?

Independent research projects in glacial environments can involve a broad range of techniques in various combinations to collect the primary and secondary data required. These include a mixture of different fieldwork techniques, laboratory techniques and desk-based techniques

Primary data sources

A fieldwork investigation into the glacial landforms present in any location may involve the following techniques:

- Field observations: this is a frequently overlooked but fundamental technique that is essential to locate and identify small glacial features such as striations that cannot be identified in remotely-sensed imagery. This typically involves the careful collection of photographs, field notes and sketches.
- Field surveys: urveys can be carried out using simple equipment such as tape measures, **Abney levels** and clinometers, or more sophisticated surveying equipment if you have access. The data can be used to generate **topographic profiles**. These surveyed profiles can provide more accurate topographic measurements of glacial landforms than can be derived from Google Earth and could be used, for example, to illustrate the profile of drumlins or to quantify the cross-sectional area of moraines.
- Field mapping: handheld GPS (see Chapter 3) can be used in conjunction with OS basemaps and can create detailed geomorphological maps that illustrate the location, extent and spatial distribution of the landforms in the study site.

Fieldwork investigations of glaciated landforms and landscapes often involve sedimentological analyses of any glacial sediments present. These analyses can be used in isolation or in combination with the geomorphological techniques listed above to aid in the description and interpretation of the glaciated landscape.

Secondary data sources

Aerial photography and remotely-sensed imagery of glacial landscapes can be acquired from various sources. This imagery can be used to explore the key characteristics and features present at a study site prior to conducting your fieldwork. Google Earth can be used in a range of ways to generate additional data which complements your own primary fieldwork data:

- *Mapping* If the resolution of the imagery is sufficiently high, Google Earth can be used to identify and map specific glacial landforms in sites you were not able to visit on foot (perhaps for safety reasons).
- *Measuring morphology* Google Earth can be used to undertake quantitative measurements of the morphology of any large landforms of interest, such as a glacial trough. The 'ruler' tool within the Google Earth software can measure the length, width and elongation of drumlins, for example.
- *Generating cross sections* The 'path' tool within Google Earth can be used to create elevation profiles that be used for example to illustrate the gradient of erosional landforms (Figure 5.21).

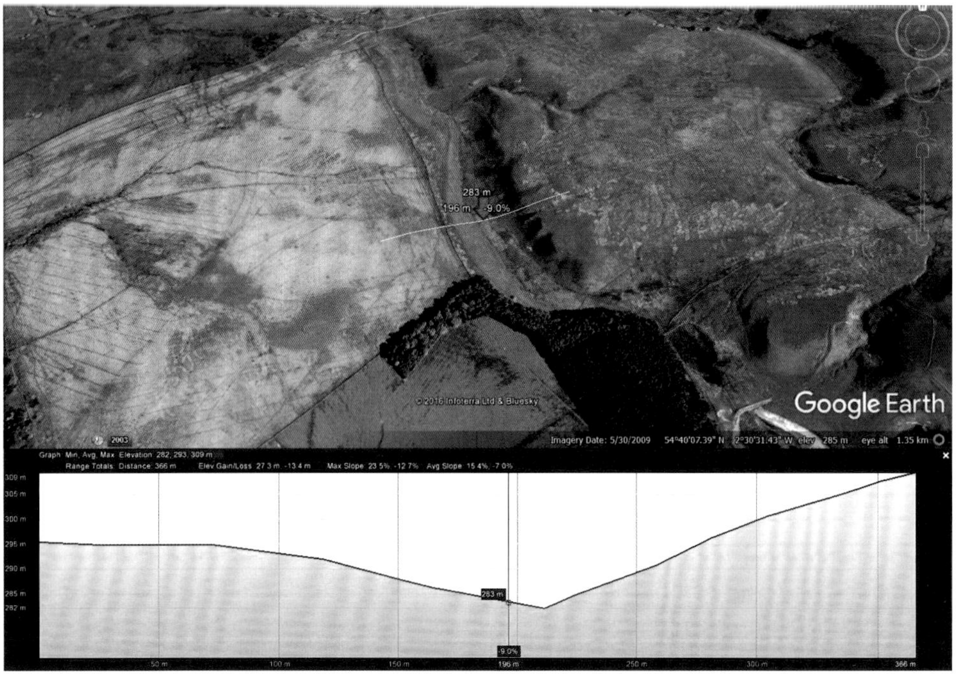

You can find a skills sheet online describing different sedimentological techniques.

Details of how to access online resources are on page 3.

Figure 5.21 A cross-sectional profile created using the Google Earth's 'add path' tool. In this case, it shows a relict glacial meltwater channel. **Source**: Google Earth

You can find an example online of data collection for a historical investigation of a glacier.

Details of how to access online resources are on page 3.

References

- Evans, D.J.A. and Benn, D. (2004) *A Practical Guide to the Study of Glacial Sediments.* Routledge: Abingdon.

- Hubbard, B. and Glasser, N. (2005) *Field Techniques in Glaciology and Glacial Geomorphology*. Wiley-Blackwell: Oxford.

- British Society of Geomorphology – Geomorphological Techniques: http://www.geomorphology.org.uk/geomorph_techniques

- Roberts M. (2013) *Geography through Enquiry*, Geographical Association: Sheffield, Chapter 5

- Lindsay, R. (2010) *Peatbogs and Carbon: A critical synthesis.* RSPB; http://www.rspb.org.uk/Images/Peatbogs_and_carbon_tcm9-255200.pdf

- Thompson, D A and Matthews R W (1989) *The storage of carbon in trees and timber* Forestry Commission http://www.forestry.gov.uk/pdf/RIN160.pdf/$FILE/RIN160.pdf

6 Evaluating your findings and presenting your work

Objectives

- *Understand how best to communicate your findings using charts, graphs, maps and tables.*

- *Understand how to construct a 'convincing' or 'well-argued' conclusion.*

- *Understand the difference between description and evaluation when concluding.*

Using graphical techniques to communicate your findings

The illustrations in this book have provided you already with a range of possible data presentation suggestions. You have also seen many instances of the use of GIS to present data in ways which we can understand quickly and easily. Used correctly, digital techniques enhance traditional mapping and graphing of data.

When trying to determine which data presentation techniques to use, remember that your primary concern is to communicate what you have discovered effectively. The role of any data presentation is to distil a mass of data into a few easy-to-interpret visual images. Exactly how you choose to present your data will depend on many of the decisions you made when planning and carrying out your data collection. This includes the type of question(s) you sought to answer, your sampling strategy, the data you collected, the methods of data collection and the character of your data (qualitative and quantitative data may be displayed very differently). You will need to work out what kinds of graphs, charts, maps, diagrams, infographics, images, texts or tables will work best in the context of your own enquiry.

There are many books and websites that offer guidance on different types of graphs and maps, including the Geographical Association's *Methods of Presenting Fieldwork Data*. There are some especially important principles which most authors will emphasise.

1. You should aim to incorporate a variety of relevant graphical techniques overall; reports which make use repetitively of only one or two kinds of chart rarely score the highest marks. Reports using a very wide range of different types of maps, graphs, diagrams, photographs and other materials are likely to score higher marks. Figure 6.1 offers further guidance on working out the best approach.

2. Quality is more important than quantity. One well-designed and relatively complex graph may impress the reader far more than many pages of simple pie charts. Some students make the mistake of including large amounts of graphs and charts which are tangential or unconnected to their main research question(s). A good rule to follow is to ask yourself: is this 'nice to know' or 'need to know' information?

3. If statistical tests such as Spearman's rank correlation and Chi-squared procedures are used to establish the significance of what your charts show, it is important to check that the data sample size is equal to or greater than the test's minimum requirements. In your conclusion, you should acknowledge the confidence level of any test result you calculate.

Over to you

Have you ever stopped and critically examined the design of your course text books? Compare two books: which has the best design and layout, and why? Which graphs and charts in these books work best in your view? Are there any poor illustrations which could be improved?

Do...	Do not...
• *frequently refer to the research question(s) you are trying to answer.* Use your data presentation to communicate your answer to the question(s) you asked as directly as possible – it can help to write down a list of what you want each data presentation to show before you start drawing them.	• *get too carried away with GIS.* The availability of spreadsheets and GIS means that you can create professional-looking graphics quickly and easily. But do not include too much superfluous information.
• *look critically at ways of communicating data used in quality newspapers and magazines.* Ask yourself whether the graphs and charts being used work well. Could you take a similar approach in your own work?	• *over-rely on the default settings in software like Microsoft Word.* You can change the colours, fonts, scales and numerous other aspects of charts and graphs. Think critically about how any changes you make could communicate your data better (you may even want to explain your choices to the reader).
• *be creative.* Just because you have not seen someone else present their data in a particular way doesn't mean you shouldn't try do so yourself. If the method communicates your findings clearly, then go for it.	• *over-complicate things.* Too many variables at once can get confusing and you need to get the balance right. Always remember that you are trying to communicate any patterns, trends, correlations or anomalies in your data as clearly as possible.
• *finish everything off properly.* Do not forget essential elements like a title, scale and key for your charts, and a north arrow for any maps you use.	• *be repetitive.* The same set of data does not need to be displayed multiple times in different ways (e.g. in a table, a bar chart and also a pie chart!). Choose one way that works well and stick with it (and perhaps justify your choice to the reader).

Figure 6.1 Guidelines for putting together an effective data presentation.

Making the most of maps

Geographical research often lends itself to mapping techniques due to the subject's disciplinary focus on spatial patterns and connections. The best maps (whether hand-drawn or computer-generated) demonstrate a sound grasp of cartographic principles and techniques, including the use of shading and colour. When making a choropleth map, it is important that the colours chosen help the viewer discern which is the highest class, and how the classes are ordered. If you look at choropleth maps in your textbooks, they often grade several tones of a single colour, such as red or blue, from dark (= more) to light (= less). Do not use large numbers of completely different colours; graphs and maps which have *too many* shading or colour classes (which sometimes become indistinguishable from one another) can become difficult to interpret.

There is often little point in including a downloaded map in a report unless it is annotated to show key places, features, issues or processes which are relevant to the study being undertaken. Adding personalised annotations to locational maps allows you to demonstrate additional map skills and to give background material in an easy-to-absorb way. This can be a very effective way to help set the scene and describe the geographic context. Do not forget also to provide the source for any non-original maps or diagrams used in reports. The source should be placed as near as possible to the diagram or map, rather than only being given in end notes (this has been done in this book).

You may decide to place your graphs and data directly onto background maps, making it easy to visualise spatial patterns. It is far better to do this than generate numerous separate bar or pie charts each showing information collected at a different sample site. Instead, overlay them all (albeit at a reduced size) on a map to create a single visual image. Patterns and spatial connections can become easier to spot when data are presented this way (Figure 6.2).

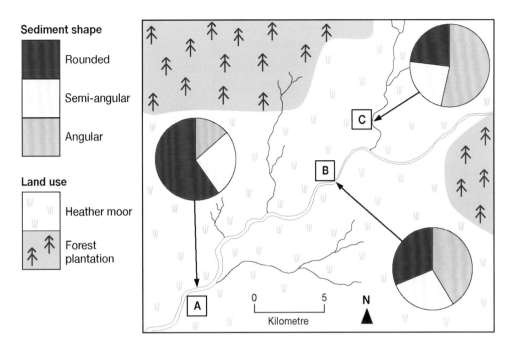

Figure 6.2 Land use and river sediment data are presented on a single map.

One final important thing to remember is that collaborative efforts between NEA students are restricted to the *collection* of relevant data. Once the information has been recorded and collated, all succeeding stages, including all data analysis, must be the *individual work* of each student. No collaboration is permitted at this stage of the process.

Evaluating and concluding your report

The time will finally arrive when you need to write the conclusion for your NEA report. There are several key rules you need to follow:
- a sound conclusion always refers back to the original fieldwork question, is based on the evidence collected and is consistent with the results and analysis
- trends, spatial patterns and any anomalies found are identified, linked and discussed comprehensively
- all concluding material should link back clearly to the data and any graphical or statistical treatment. Anomalies should be explained, not simply ignored or ascribed to some form of observer error
- where appropriate, conclusions may examine different perspectives in relation to the specific fieldwork question and the established geographical theory and context.

You can also offer a sensible evaluation of your enquiry, with valid suggestions for improvements. These suggestions may relate to the choice of case study context, the methods and equipment used, or any other aspect of the research process. Suggesting that more data could have been collected or greater care taken will not impress your reader, however. A good critical evaluation will dig deeper than that. For instance, with hindsight, how satisfactory were the: equipment used; size and selection of sample; location and time of surveys; quality and quantity of data? Try to show you have thought deeply about potential or real flaws in the methods used. You may even consider how the original fieldwork question or hypothesis might be modified or improved in light of what you have since discovered.

Figure 6.3 shows an extract from the criteria used in one A level geography specification to award marks for the 'conclusions and critical evaluation' which must feature at the end of any NEA report. As you can see, the criteria show that a great deal is expected. More is anticipated than a simple description of your findings and a stated 'yes' or 'no' answer (in relation to the research questions you asked).

Level 4	19-24 marks (24 is the maximum mark available)	• **Synthesises** research findings coherently and comprehensively. • Provides a **balanced appraisal** of the reliability of evidence and validity of conclusions. • A balanced and concise, **well-developed argument** is expressed through sustained logical lines of reasoning that demonstrates use of a structured and comprehensive enquiry process. • Uses accurate geographical **terminology** throughout. • **Convincing conclusions** that are fully supported by drawing together a selection of relevant evidence and concepts linked to the entire purpose of the investigation.

Figure 6.3 Selected marking criteria for the 'conclusions and critical evaluation' element of the NEA. **Source**: Edexcel

Top Tip
Do not add lots of new information to your conclusion
Avoid introducing entirely new ideas, theories or data as part of your conclusion. All important information – be they primary or secondary data – should have been written about earlier in the report.

Figure 6.4 shows two contrasting styles of conclusion. In this case, a student has completed a study of variations in urban house prices as part of an investigation into urban inequality. Conclusion B is by far the superior of the two approaches. In particular, note how:

- Conclusion A is descriptive in style and consists of simple list-like and mostly unconnected statements. In contrast, conclusion B synthesises (draws together) different findings to create a more convincing picture.
- Conclusion A does not reflect critically on what is being argued at any stage. Conclusion B is far more balanced and evaluative in this respect.
- Conclusion A does not reflect on the validity and reliability of the findings, whereas conclusion B does.

Figure 6.4 Contrasting ways of writing the conclusion for a report dealing with urban inequality and house prices.

Conclusion A – descriptive	**Conclusion B – evaluative**
In conclusion, my research showed that • prices were very high in Palace Riverside • prices were lower in Parson's Green • prices were lowest in Fulham Broadway. The actual figures showed that house prices for a two-bed flat varied from almost a million pounds in the richest areas to half that in other areas (**1**). I also found that environmental quality varied greatly between the three survey areas. The highest values were found where house prices are also highest. The lowest values were found where the lowest house prices were (**2**). I have therefore answered my question 'how and why do house prices vary in Fulham' (**3**) by showing that they vary a great deal and that this is because there is so much variation in environmental quality (as my surveys showed). I think that my results were very reliable although if I had more time it would been good to carry out a larger sample and to take more readings of environmental quality. (**4**)	There were significant differences in property prices in the three study areas in Fulham. This strongly suggests that average incomes vary between the three study areas. This corroborates what the 2011 Census data also showed about inequality in Fulham. (**1**) Prices in Palace Riverside were typically 50% higher than in Fulham Broadway, with Parson's Green somewhere in between. I am 99% confident these observed differences are real, following the use of the Chi-squared test. (**2**) There was also a clear correlation between price variations and environmental quality in the three districts. High prices seem to be closely related to proximity to parks and the river, and parking space provision – although it is possible that there are other causal factors I have not been able to uncover. If I were to repeat the work I would additionally examine how these places are represented in the media. (**3**) Finally, my conclusions are tentative because I used semi–qualitative data (the quality index) which involved making subjective judgements. (**4**)
Marker's comments (**1**) Results are listed. (**2**) Simple causal link established. (**3**) Refers back to original research question – good. (**4**) Very basic improvement suggested that does not reflect critically on the research process.	**Marker's comments** (**1**) Strengthens the case being made by synthesising (linking) the primary and secondary data findings. (**2**) Establishes a statistical level of confidence. (**3**) Rightly questions the validity of the conclusion. (**4**) Acknowledges limitations of methods in a balanced way using specialist terms

Editing and formatting your report

It is always a great shame when good material suffers from poor presentation. To optimise your chances of success, make every effort you can to edit, format, print and present your work as professionally as you can and in 'reader-friendly' ways.

- Editing your words involves removing superfluous sentences and words. Avoid repetition and follow the conventions of grammar and punctuation.

- Formatting means making the right choice and size of font (Calibri, Ariel and Times New Roman are popular and uncontroversial choices). Avoid mixing too many different fonts. Consider also setting the line spacing at 1.5. This wider spacing is used in many professional reports and makes the text easier to read. Figure 6.5 shows two contrasting types of formatting. Which is more reader-friendly?

- Take care to number all illustrations sequentially and to provide a title for every map, graph, chart and photograph. Use the Harvard style of referencing in your bibliography (endnotes) or footnotes. (see Chapter 1, Top Tip on page 11).

- Oversize fold-out diagrams and other non-standard forms of presentation can add interest to a report but try not to include excessively large maps that it will be difficult for the reader to inspect. Look at your textbooks and find the largest-sized map or graphic they contain. Is there any compelling need for your own graphics to be larger? If you have produced large diagrams and maps by hand you may be able to scan and print them at a reduced size (which may make them look even more detailed!).

- You may want to include a 'header' on each page (use the 'help' feature in Word to find out how). You can also change the margin settings in Word to 'narrow' which allows you to place more material on each page and use larger diagrams.

- Do not include material in an appendix that is of central importance to the report and which really belongs in the body of the report. Appendices should be used only for non-essential material such as an example of a completed questionnaire (there is no need to include all of your completed questionnaires).

- When you print your document, consider using double-sided printing. It might make it easier for the reader to compare two illustrations on opposite facing pages. Also, you might try to avoid the use of a large and heavy ring binder by opting instead for a lightweight plastic folder or stapled pages with a strengthened spine. Teachers and moderators might prefer *not* to be handling needlessly bulky and heavy reports.

Figure 6.5 Choosing the right style of document presentation.

Due to the limitations of conducting a physical geography investigation in central Manchester, the Victorian cemetery proved an ideal study ground because of the excellent critical analysis the limestone gravestones can provide. The stones' length of exposure is immediately calculable from the year of death inscription they carry. All stones have been used here since the foundation of the cemetery, again making it a useful choice. It is one of the largest cemeteries in the city, and allowed me to find a wide range of data. A substantial data set was required that would enable me to create a representative and stratified sample. In total, I collected 180 headstone recordings from the *non-vegetated (open)*, west-facing areas. My rationale for this was that (1) the majority of stones faced westwards, hence a larger sample was possible and (2) 'non vegetated' stones would not be under tree cover which might impact upon weathering. I was also concerned about seasonal changes in …

Poor communication (tiny font, no line spacing and no paragraphs)

Due to the limitations of conducting a physical geography investigation in central Manchester, the Victorian cemetery proved an ideal study ground because of the excellent critical analysis the limestone gravestones can provide.

The stones' length of exposure is immediately calculable from the year of death inscription they carry. All stones have been used here since the foundation of the cemetery, again making it a useful choice. It is one of the largest cemeteries in the city, and allowed me to find a wide range of data.

Good communication (larger text, 1.5 line spacing and more frequent paragraphing)

The right length

Most important of all, do not exceed the total word count. A maximum of 4,000 words has been recommended. You will not be penalised for exceeding the recommended length; marks will not be subtracted for instance. However, the official guidance is that any response differing *significantly* from the recommended length will become self-penalising, this most likely reason being a lack of focus, coherence and concision. The best reports will undoubtedly remain within the word limit and will impress by the way they explain and evaluate what has been done *succinctly*.

The discipline you need to show extends to the use of tables, boxes and footnotes. Almost all the words in tables do count towards the total word count. The inclusion of excessive amounts of superfluous boxed material could prevent some candidates from gaining higher marks. You may be familiar with the old saying: 'I can't see the wood for the trees'. Make sure the reader does not think this when reading your report!

Mission accomplished!

Provided you adhere to most of the presentation guidelines provided in this chapter, there is every chance you will make a success of your individual investigation. Figure 6.6 offers a final checklist covering the whole enquiry pathway from start to finish.

Do not forget to...
✓ Choose a tightly-focused fieldwork question and, if relevant, a strictly limited number of hypotheses.
✓ Link the fieldwork question clearly with your geography specification.
✓ Ensure that your proposed work has a clear spatial component and ideally involves collecting data that you can represent on maps ideally. Be careful not to carry out what is essentially a biology or economics investigation!
✓ Make sure you know all about the 'specialised concepts' – such as risk and threshold – and how they can be used.
✓ Personalise any downloaded maps to show the location, choice of topic and/or sample points, following standard geographic conventions such as including a scale and north arrow.
✓ Justify (in detail) all the methods used and explain the sampling method(s) employed.
✓ Ensure that ample quantitative data is collected for graphs. Limit the application of statistical tests such as Spearman's rank correlation to situations where sufficient data has been collected.
✓ Be aware of the wide range of graphical techniques and simple statistical tools which are available for your data analysis. Fieldwork investigations benefit when a variety of techniques are used.
✓ Avoid using extensive tables in reports, especially in the sections for methods and evaluation. Incorporate a wide variety of appropriate graphical and mapping techniques in your analysis.
✓ Focus in the analysis on interpreting (not just describing) results and explaining your findings, focusing on any spatial patterns or trends identified.
✓ Number and place all the illustrations appropriately within the text, and then refer to them throughout the written analysis.
✓ Pay close attention to the assessment criteria and follow the recommended report structure.
✓ Print and present your finished report in a light and user-friendly format.

Figure 6.6 Individual investigation checklist.
Source: Tony Burton

Reference

• St John, P. and Richardson, D. (1997) *Methods of Presenting Fieldwork Data*. Geographical Association. Available at: http://www.geography.org.uk/shop

Glossary

Abney level — a type of clinometer that is used for measuring angles of inclination

aggregate tool — **GIS** tools that create an average value

anthropogenic — produced by, originating from human activity

attitudinal data — information about people's attitudes: their opinions or perceptions of something

attribute — in **GIS**, further information recorded about a location

base map — the background map that data are displayed on

behavioural data — information about people's behaviour: what they do, for example how often they shop in a location

bias — something that influences the selection of data in a way that risks making a measurement unrepresentative or unreliable; writing which is overly influenced by the authors' personal feelings or interests

buffer — in **GIS**, buffer tools create areas around a point, line or area up to a specified distance

Cailleux Index — a score of 1000 on this index would indicate a perfectly spherical pebble. The lower the index score, the more angular the pebble.

cartography — making maps

categorical — data that are grouped in categories, e.g. male and female

causality — the relationship between a cause and the effects or impacts it has

Census — the official process of counting a country's population and finding out about it. In the UK, Censuses are held every ten years, the last were in 2011.

choropleth — a thematic map that uses shading or patterns to indicate the average value of something in an area

citing — referencing sources, e.g. in a literature review

clinometer — an instrument used to measure the angle of a slope

coding — a tool used to extract meaningful data from open responses to questionnaire questions

confounding variables — something other than the variable you are testing which could also possibly affect the result. Confounding variables need to be controlled for, or at least documented and discussed

contextualise — to consider something together with the events, situation or other information that relates to it, rather than just on its own

cumecs — cubic metres per second, as a unit for measuring the rate of flow of water

Cumulative (running) mean — a series of averages taken from smaller subsets of a larger dataset to provide a 'running total' of average results so far

deductive — developing a hypothesis based on existing knowledge and understanding first and then collecting data to test that hypothesis (compare with **inductive**)

enumeration district — an administrative district that used to be used in **Census**-taking

equilibrium — a state of balance between outputs and inputs

ethnography — the study of people and places

flux — a flow of gas, liquid or solid matter resulting in a transfer between two locations

formal representation — a representation of place produced by a recognised authority, e.g. a council, tourist board or university

frequency data — information on the number of times something happened in an enquiry or experiment

geomorphological — relating to the study of landforms and the processes that form and shape them

geospatial — data that are associated with particular geographic locations

geospatial technology — geospatial technology is software and hardware used to visualise, measure and analyse data that are associated with geographic locations

geotagging — attaching a location (latitude and longitude) to a file so that it can be located on a map

GIS — Geographical Information Systems: computer-based methods of collecting, storing, sorting, manipulating, analysing and presenting spatial information (information that can be mapped)

GPS — a space-based navigation system that provides location and time information anywhere on Earth

heterogeneous — consisting of things (or people) that are each different from each other

homogeneous — consisting of things (or people) that are all the same

hypothesis — a specific, focused, directional statement of what you expect to find

inductive — collecting data or observations first and then seeking to find a pattern to explain them afterwards (compare with **deductive**)

informal representation — a representation of place not from a formal authority; likely to represent the views and feelings of a single author

layer	GIS works by building up multiple layers of information
line	in GIS, a series of points joined to create a line
location	a particular place
macro trend	a trend (e.g. a social or economic trend) on a very large, often global, scale, e.g. globalisation
mental map	how a person perceives their area, their own personal representation of a place
methodology	specific methods and principles used when investigating something
normal distribution	when data are spread symmetrically around the median value, so most data values are clustered in the middle and extremely small and extremely large data values are rare. When plotted on a chart it produces a bell-shaped curve.
normalised	data that have been made comparable by converting them all to the same unit, e.g. percentages
objective	not influenced by opinions, emotions, personal feelings or bias
ordinal	data that mixes numerical and categorical data, for example when categories are given a number or score
orthodox	ideas and theories that are generally accepted as being correct
pilot survey	a survey carried out on a small scale to test survey techniques or assumptions before carrying out the larger-scale survey
place meaning	a combination of the real and perceived characteristics of a geographical space
place profile	a picture of the social, economic and environmental facets of a place that is being studied, built up using different fieldwork techniques
place representation	descriptions of a place and its identity: see formal representation and informal representation
point	in GIS, a single location defined by one pair of coordinates
polygon	in GIS, a series of coordinates which have been joined together producing a closed shape
primary data	first-hand data collected by students themselves
proxy data	data that are used to stand in for something that cannot be directly measured. For example, the width of tree rings can be used as proxy data for measurements of past climatic conditions
quadrat	a square metre of ground selected at random for sampling, e.g. plant species. Often selected using a metre-square frame
qualitative data	non-numerical, descriptive data which may be obtained from personal observation (noting behaviour, field-sketching, photographs, etc.) analysing printed/audio-visual material or investigating people's opinion, attitudes and beliefs
quantitative data	numerical data, often obtained through measurement, questionnaires or from public secondary databases
raster data	raster data represent the world by dividing it into grid squares
rebranding	a deliberate effort to market a place as desirable for investment and visitors
regeneration	attempts to change a place by attracting new economic activity and investment to it or trying to stimulate local enterprise and entrepreneurship there
reimaging	an attempt to represent a place in new ways, the cultural reinvention of a place
remote sensing	collecting data from afar, e.g. satellite or aerial photography
representative	when a sample of something accurately reflects the larger population it is taken from it is said to be representative of that larger population
sampling population	the population a representative sample is being taken of
secondary data	information that has already been collected by someone else
skewed data	data that are altered in a way that is unrepresentative
spatial	relating to where things are in space, their position, size, shape, etc.
subjective	influenced by opinions, emotions, personal feelings, biased
summarise tool	GIS tools that create an average value
synthesis	linking things together, the process of combining things or something made by combining things together
threshold	a 'tipping point' in a natural or social system after which the system shifts radically into a different equilibrium (balance)
topographic profile	a 'side view' or cross-section view of a landscape along a specific line through that landscape
tracer	a fieldwork technique for measuring longshore drift, which involves marking sand with different colours
transcript	a written record of what was said in an interview conversation
transect	a line along which data is collected
triangulation	checking data collected from one source by comparing it with data collected from other sources
vector data	coordinate-based locations (with a collection of attributes attached to every place or location